RURAL NUTRITION
IN CHINA

RURAL NUTRITION
IN CHINA

R. O. WHYTE

HONG KONG
OXFORD UNIVERSITY PRESS
LONDON NEW YORK
1972

Oxford University Press, Ely House, London W.I

GLASGOW NEW YORK TORONTO MELBOURNE WELLINGTON
CAPE TOWN IBADAN NAIROBI DAR ES SALAAM LUSAKA ADDIS ABABA
DELHI BOMBAY CALCUTTA MADRAS KARACHI LAHORE DACCA
KUALA LUMPUR SINGAPORE HONG KONG TOKYO

News Building, North Point, Hong Kong

© *Oxford University Press 1972*

*Printed by Dai Nippon Printing Co. (Int'l) Ltd.
1 Pat Tat Street, Kowloon, Hong Kong*

Contents

Figures

Tables

I
The Approach

China in Monsoon Asia

SPECIALISTS in the production, distribution and utilization of food are profoundly interested in the nutrition of the urban and rural peoples of the Chinese People's Republic. It is impossible to define precisely the actual situation in China because the basic data are almost wholly lacking. Nor is it possible to be even approximately exact in estimating the degrees, if any, of under-nutrition and/or malnutrition in the absence of the essential dietary surveys and their associated clinical and biochemical examinations.

Throughout Asia, authorities are planning nutritional policies on the basis of known and proven facts of human requirements, of the actual and potential availability of foods, and of the relation between nutrition and the health, physical and mental well-being of their people.[1]

The isolation of China has tended to create the belief that China is somehow fundamentally different from the rest of the world. It is thought that the problems of land use, agriculture and human nutrition are in some way unique and that greater production of food is not subject to the same natural laws and hazards that apply in the rest of Asia. As is shown below, this is not so. The more densely populated and hence the most critical parts of China are part of Monsoon Asia. The land systems or eco-systems, the soils, the climax and secondary forms of vegetation, the crops and cropping systems, domestic livestock and types of animal husbandry, and the pests and diseases which affect production, are all those of that vast region of Asia that has a monsoonal eco-climate. Some scholars consider that 'greater South-East Asia' extends up to the Tsinling Mountains in China (Lebar, Hickey and Musgrave, 1964). The place of China in the meteorological

pattern of Asia has been confirmed by the meteorologists of the Academia Sinica (see Chapter III and Figs. 5 and 6).

It is fully recognized that anyone who attempts to assess the situation in China without a first-hand knowledge of the country and of the written language must proceed with caution. It is, however, possible, with twenty years' experience of monsoonal land use, agriculture and animal husbandry in the region from West Pakistan to Japan, to discuss the problems and potentialities of the Chinese land and the health of its people on the basis of comparable conditions elsewhere. The limited data on production available from China itself up to mid-1970[2] have also been used in the assessment of the nutritional status of the rural people, and especially of the vulnerable groups. Few now remain from the former generation of non-Chinese specialists in agriculture and human health and nutrition whose long familiarity with the Chinese land, peoples and languages so eminently qualified them to speak of conditions they knew. A new review based on modern scientific knowledge in agriculture and nutrition would seem to be essential.

Bardhan's (1970) broad comparison of recent policy and performance in Chinese and Indian agriculture may serve to put things into perspective, as a sequel to earlier comparative studies (Ishikawa, 1967; Malenbaum, 1959; Raj, 1967). Bardhan refers to the fact that in both countries the availability and reliability of economic information are at their worst in respect of agriculture (for reasons of non-availability, continuous changes in coverage and reporting systems, occasional deliberate mis-reporting, lack of impartiality). Nevertheless, it is possible to extract some comparative data from Bardhan's study, which relates to the period 1952/3 to 1967/8 (Table 1).

---

[1] The situation in Asia as a whole is being reviewed in a forthcoming book by the same author entitled *Rural Nutrition in Monsoon Asia*.

[2] Including access to monitored Chinese press reports and radio broadcasts up to mid-1970.

The maximum biological productivity that can be achieved with full use of inputs, under dry land conditions (100 per cent utilization), and the high levels that can theoretically be obtained with full and correct use of irrigation water (200 per cent utilization in the north with monsoonal summers and temperate winters, and 300 per cent in the monsoonal southern provinces) is governed by the environment in all its macro- and micro-manifestations—the cyclic and seasonal fluctuation between excess, adequacy and deficit in rainfall, combined with a range of maximum and minimum temperatures. Political and economic determinism in a developing country can operate only within the limits imposed by the environment. The most important and perhaps the most unpredictable component of the rural ecosystem is man.

Where Chinese agriculture today differs from that of its neighbours in Monsoon Asia is in the form of political and administrative organization, the efficiency of extraction of food from the rural areas for the urban centres, industrial communities, those rural areas producing industrial crops such as cotton and soybean, and the military, to the detriment of standards of rural nutrition (as also happens with a market economy), and in the comparative incentives to work among the cultivators of a centrally directed regime.

The physiological characteristics and food habits of a people change only exceedingly slowly, even if new foods become available and are accepted as part of the cropping pattern or of the diet. We have no reason to suppose that any new foods have become part of the regular diet of rural Chinese. There is an extensive literature on Chinese health, food habits and practices up to about twenty years ago. Much work has been done more recently on the present nutritional status and practices of the overseas Chinese. Thus it is possible to make a fairly accurate assessment of the nutritional requirements and responses of the rural people of mainland China.

In spite of the absence of data or publications on rural nutrition in China today, it is possible to show what facts and factors have to be considered in an assessment of the situation. One may draw conclusions which, although necessarily tentative, are more closely related to the criteria of modern nutritional science than the assumptions which are based on actual or hypothetical figures of cereal production alone—on quantity, without due consideration of quality in foods. In the absence of any reliable data from China on production since 1959, it is necessary to consider the position from the opposite angle, that is, to express accepted nutritional targets per head of population per day or per year, in terms of the hectares of land or the numbers of livestock needed to produce these amounts of food. These may be equated against the estimates of production made by outside observers as referred to below.

Definition of Urban and Rural Communities

The rural peoples are selected for study because they produce the food for urban administrators and industrial segments of the population. The welfare and nutrition of the rural people are the key to national economic development, both agrarian and industrial, and in fact to national survival. If the rural peoples fail or become too apathetic to work, China fails. Emphasis on the importance of the rural peoples has been a basic tenet of the philosophy of many Asian reformers, including Mao Tse-tung and Mahatma Gandhi.

A State Resolution of the Chinese People's Republic in 1955 defined urban and rural areas (Chen, 1966):

Urban areas (towns and cities) are those where a municipal people's council or a people's council of the *hsien* level or above is located, except for mobile administrative units in the pastoral areas. Urban areas are also those with 2,000 inhabitants or more, of whom at least half are engaged in pursuits other than agriculture. Places of 1,000 to 2,000 population may also be classified as urban, provided these are industrial, commercial, transport, educational or research centres, or are residential areas of workers, and provided at least 75 per cent of the population is non-agricultural. Finally, places with sanatorium facilities in which patients constitute more than half of the local permanent population may also be classified as urban. All other areas are considered rural. The same criteria are applied to city suburbs. They are rural if the majority of the population is engaged in agriculture.

It would be appropriate in a nutritional study on China, with its special system for the procure-

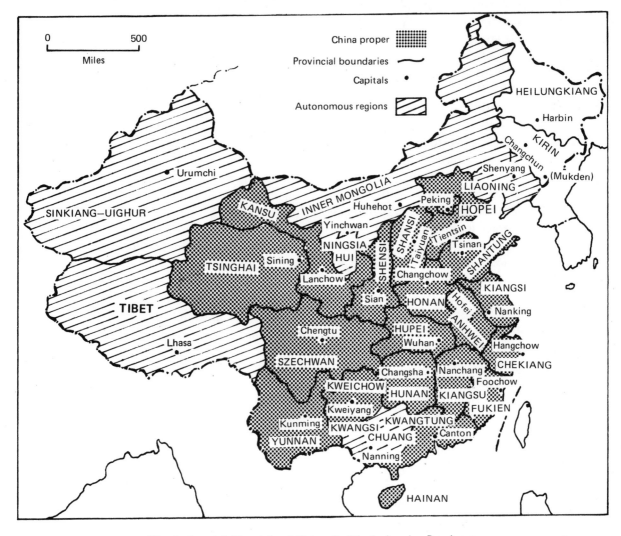

Fig. 1   People's Republic of China: Political, showing Provinces

ment and distribution of foodgrains, to distinguish first, between rural communities whose foodgrain allotment represents a share of what they themselves have produced, or is given in exchange for some commodity such as soybeans or cotton which they have produced; and secondly, between urban communities, who grow no food for themselves, and who are entirely dependent on allocations from the State foodgrain pool.

The Vulnerable Groups

Among the rural people, the correct nutrition of the vulnerable groups within the community must receive priority if the children of the present

are to become capable citizens of the future, fully developed and strong in body and brain capacity. The vulnerable groups are usually defined as including infants and children of pre-school age (1 to 6 years), pregnant and nursing mothers, and the sick. Where diets are known to be unsatisfactory, probably all women of reproductive age should be included. School children and adolescents also have special needs. It is increasingly being recognized that these groups need particular consideration in nutrition policies, especially where resources of plant and animal protein are in deficit; the welfare of the present and future generations of children demands that limited supplies of the acceptable forms of protein, particularly those of animal origin, should be reserved for the vulnerable groups.

Rural Dietary Patterns

Throughout Asia, the rural peoples depend upon foods produced locally. Maps of regional agroclimatic zones, of systems of land use, and of the crops and domestic livestock therefore also indicate rural dietary patterns, particularly with regard to the staple foods. In China it is only in years of crisis caused by climatic fluctuations or other factors that food is brought in from elsewhere, as a temporary loan to be repaid in subsequent years. Food also has to be provided where the cultivators have to concentrate on the production of non-food crops. Change in dietary habits and status will occur only where marked change in farming techniques and crops takes place, for example, following the introduction of irrigation. 'The end result of the type of land utilization of a country is the standard of living it provides for its population' (Low, 1937).

This study is concerned with balance in the diet. It is assumed that China will ensure sufficient foodgrain consumption per caput from domestic and imported sources to meet calorie requirements. Therefore the main considerations here are the intakes of protein, vitamins, minerals and fats, much of which are, of course, provided by the foodgrains. It is necessary first to review briefly the land resources; then the nutritional requirements of different sections of the population; the composition of rural diets and the sources of their ingredients; and the extent to which nutritional targets are likely to be met.

No attempt is made to give estimates of intake per caput of calories or nutrients. No respectable information for such a purpose exists; one would need accurate weighing and laboratory analyses of cooked foods consumed over several days at different seasons of the year by the different social and age groups in all the many ecoclimatic regions of China. It is true that it has become fashionable for countries to take figures for total grain production, decide on availability per caput and from this, with no knowledge whatsoever of

intake of other essential foods, to calculate calorie, sometimes even nutrient intakes. Even as an approximately accurate indicator of true food intake, and therefore of status of nutrition, this is an exercise in statistical fantasy.

It seems that diets deteriorated in quantity and quality during the period when the communes were first set up, and improved following the reintroduction of the private plots. Recently, however, both refugees from and visitors to China report widespread complaints of hunger—everyone has food but no one has enough. It must be remembered that large sections of the population are engaged in continuous heavy labour, with a high calorie requirement which is perhaps not met by present rations.

A Changed Way of Life

Rural life in China has changed more profoundly during the past twenty years than it has done for centuries. Order has been brought into the chaos inherited by the present regime. The countryside is safe from marauding bandits, wandering soldiers and inter-village feuds. Water control prevents flooding in many areas where this was an annual event. Careful controls and improved communications have combined to eliminate the hunger previously associated with crop failure, since grains may be moved into deficit areas. The currency with which the cultivator is paid for his produce and buys his few needs is a stable one; corruption has been rooted out. Villages are cleaner, and consequently healthier than before. Many have been electrified.

Beliefs which were formerly of fundamental importance to society have been attacked as superstition, especially where they involved unproductive use of family or community resources. Images have been destroyed, and temples and ancestral halls used for secular purposes. Heavy expenditure on ceremonies celebrating the major events of life is discouraged and ancestor worship frowned upon. Burial according to geomantic principles, involving as it did the sterilization of valuable agricultural land in the plains, is no longer allowed, while old sites have been re-opened for cultivation.

The life of the women has been transformed from an existence which, even if they escaped early death or a number of distressing alternatives dictated by the poverty of their parents, was physically and mentally circumscribed. It is no longer true that 'an incompetent man can get about in nine counties, but a competent woman can only get around her kitchen stove'. In many areas factory work has absorbed the rural unemployed and under-employed, while public works ensure that there are few idle hands in China in seasons when the demand for agricultural labour is less.

All these achievements have led some to wonder if the concomitant tightly organized lives and erosion of traditional values will continue to be acceptable to generations who did not experience the hardships of twenty or thirty years ago. Freedman (1958, 1966) has shown that the big lineages were rooted in land ownership, and are unlikely to have survived in their traditional form. Nonetheless, it is clear from the mainland Press that attempts to 'change the minds of the people' are not yet successful, either in sublimating primary concern for the family with concern for the community and nation, or in convincing people that manual and agricultural labour is as dignified as scholarly attainment—the source of lineage pride and advancement in the past.

Other observers are so moved by achievements so far that they accept some of the more legendary claims of a regime which, by example, is trying to encourage its vast population to maintain the momentum and enthusiasm of early years. In the present study, we may perhaps paraphrase Professor Freedman[3] and say that, in order to assess the most recent developments of nutrition, health and agriculture in China, we need to have as much trust in our common sense as suspicion of the few 'facts' offered to us.

[3] Professor Freedman wrote (1966): 'In order to handle the most recent phase of the modern history of the Chinese lineage, we need to have as much trust in our imagination as suspicion of the few "facts" offered to us.'

Land Resources for Food Production

Production and Distribution of Foodgrains

ANY study of present status and possible future developments in rural nutrition must necessarily begin with a review of the land resources. This can be done only briefly in the present context. The emphasis is more on the technical aspects of land use and crop and livestock husbandry than on the administrative measures designed to stimulate production in constantly changing national and provincial policies.

The major objective of China's policy is, of course, the provision of foodgrains for the urban and rural people. As is shown below, this aspect is only of marginal interest in the present review of quality in the diet. Reference should be made to Donnithorne's study of output, procurement, transfers and trade (1970), and of the influence of factors such as transport difficulties and lack of storage facilities on the procurement programme. It appears that each province and the urban areas within each province are largely dependent upon the production of that province. Her conclusion in respect of foodgrains is, with a population of 750 million and a grain output of 190 million metric tons in 1967, output per head would have been 253 kg. per annum,[1] 'marginal, perhaps just sufficient, if evenly spread. The same output with a higher population figure would give an overall deficiency in grain.' In translating these figures into consumption per head, allowance should be made for the amount of grain used for seed, livestock feed and export, for brewing and other industrial uses and for losses during transport and storage after harvest. The amount imported should be added to the gross production figure (Table 12).

As is shown in the present study, Donnithorne's conclusion about the increased contri-

[1] For further estimates, see Chapter IX.

bution of vegetables, meat and eggs to a falling caloric intake is highly debatable:

On most outside estimates of China's grain output and population for the last few years, consumption per person must have declined since 1957, yet it is thought that in the areas from which information is available, the per capita calory intake of food is roughly the same as in 1957. This has come about as a result of the increase in output of vegetables, meat and eggs, thus representing an improvement in the quality of the diet. These subsidiary foodstuffs have been grown largely on the private plots which flourished in the 'Liuist' period of 1962-65 and which do not seem to have been seriously reduced, in most places, during the Cultural Revolution.

More ominous in terms of quality in the diet is her suggestion that the supply of grain from other parts of China for the great cities and for the deficit provinces might no longer be organized by administrative measures, but left to the influence of market forces:

The difficulties encountered by Peking in trying to extract grain from surplus provinces would not occur if both centre and provinces permitted the bulk of the harvest to be sold on the free market. At present while a fairly legitimate, no more than grey, free market exists for grain, only small quantities apparently seep through on to it. With a larger free market in grain, resources (private plots, labour, fertilizers, etc.) at present devoted to vegetable and livestock production might be switched to grain.

The comparison of Chinese and Indian agriculture made by Bardhan (1970) considers grain production, rates of growth in production and yields, soil nutrients, potential and effective irrigation, vulnerability to floods and droughts, economics, use of labour and the proportion of foodgrain production extracted from rural areas. It is to be hoped that someone with access to more recent data will bring Table 1 up to date. There have been considerable developments in both China and India since the period 1965 to 1968. Bardhan's conclusions are:

For India one can, no doubt, expect that with the significant improvement in supplies of agricultural inputs and investment, Indian agricultural performance may be much better in the next decade than it has been in the past. But a large part of her development effort will remain seriously constrained by her backward institutional framework and archaic administrative setup.

Whether or not the better potential for China will be effectively used will depend to a large degree on whether from time to time the Party does or does not avoid the temptation to force the pace of things in the face of technical feasibility, to go in for hastily conceived crash programs, or to bring about further reorganizations of land institutions without due consideration of peasant incentives.

No comparative study of two economies is complete without a consideration of the distribution patterns, but we have chosen not to discuss it here out of considerations of space as well as our belief that most people will hardly deny that the pattern of income and wealth is likely to be more egalitarian in China than in India. We may only note that the welfare effects of a more egalitarian distribution may be substantial in countries like India or China with millions of people at the near-subsistence level of consumption.

Land Classification

The China of today is an outcome of the basic ecological distinction between the grassland west and the forest east (Wang, 1961) (Fig. 4). In the now deforested and heavily populated east, one finds the following types of man-made land use upon which most of the population now depends (Fig. 3):

(a) districts in which over half of the total land is cultivated

(b) where over a quarter of the land is cultivated, and

(c) where there are patches of cultivation with forest and scrubland on the uplands.

Land types and farming systems can be regarded as indicators of agricultural potential, and therefore in varying degree, of the standards of human nutrition to be expected in the rural areas. Examples are the pioneer classification of J. Lossing Buck and his colleagues (1937) (see Figs. 2 and 3), and the recent demarcation of agricultural China into four major regions (or first cate-

TABLE 1 Comparison of Chinese and Indian Agriculture in the Period 1952/3 to 1967/8

	China		India	
	1955	*1965*	*1955*	*1965*
Gross sown acreage under all crops (million ha.)	151.1	156	144.1	157.9
Index of multiple cropping (gross sown acreage under all crops) (percentage)	137.2	143.1	112.8	114.8
	1952	*1965*	*1952*	*1965*
Yields per hectare in processed foodgrains (metric tons) *rice*	1.78	2.19	0.81	1.07
wheat	0.62	0.72	0.78	0.9
all foodgrains	1.11	1.3	0.59	0.75
Production of processed foodgrains (million metric tons)	124.9	161.8	61.67	89.0
Production of foodgrains in kg. per caput per annum	217.2	222.3	164.0	182.0
	1952 to 1967		*1952/3 to 1967/8*	
Annual (compound) rate of growth of output of foodgrains (per cent)	2.7		3.0	
Linear regression analysis on bases of year-to-year output of data for growth rate (per cent)	1.9		1.7	
	1955	*1965*	*1955/6*	*1964/5*
Consumption of chemical fertilizers per hectare of gross cropped area ($N + P_2O_5 + K_2O$ in kg.)	1.7	10.2	0.9	4.9

Source: Bardhan, 1970.

TABLE 2   Characteristics of the Major Agricultural Regions

	North-east	South-east	North-west	Tibet-Chinghai	Total
Total arable land	52.0	44.1	3.2	0.7	100
Wet rice	6.2	93.3	0.5	—	100
Vegetable oils	45.2	52.5	1.9	0.4	100
Total food production	35.8	61.2	2.5	0.5	100
Total cotton production	57.0	39.5	3.5	—	100
Number of cattle	30.1	53.6	4.6	11.7	100
Number of pigs	31.5	67.7	0.5	0.3	100
Number of sheep	36.2	8.1	27.0	28.7	100
Number of goats	52.1	24.2	13.4	10.3	100
Agricultural population	35.1	63.0	1.4	0.5	100
Land per caput (mou)[a]	4.6	2.2	6.9	4.1	3.1

Source: Teng, 1963

[a] 15 mou = approx. one hectare

gory regions) leading to a total of 129 regions of the fourth category (Table 2) (Teng, 1963). A zonation of the country has also been attempted on the basis of actual and target production per unit area: zone 1 (north) from 990 to 2,640 kg. per ha.; zone 2 (central China) 1,373 to 3,300 kg. per ha.; zone 3 (south) 2,640 to 5,280 kg. per ha. (Tregear, 1965).

Donnithorne (1970) states that in the 1960s, the central Government has been more inclined to spend its funds where they would produce the best yield—in terms of central interest—where a large surplus of grain or of industrial crops could be relied upon. Thus investment in agriculture has been concentrated in the 'areas of high and stable yield', from which off-farm procurement would be greatest. These were in any case the more prosperous agricultural districts. Thus the policy of preference for the best areas may be politically and economically correct, but it must have increased regional income differentiation rather than reduced it. These areas receive priority for investment grants and agricultural credit, for rural electrification and for the allocation of fertilizers and agricultural machinery. The expansion of manufacture of field machinery reported in mid-1970 will probably also be for use in the best areas. Thus the central Government would be justified in claiming a good part of the increased yields:

These areas appear to have been fulfilling the same role as the 'key economic areas' of earlier periods of Chinese history which provided the imperial administration with grain for the capital and the army. These areas designated as major grain and cotton areas included the deltas of the Yangtze and the Pearl Rivers, the Hangchow-Kashing-Huchow area of Chekiang, the Han River Valley in Hupeh, the Chengtu Plain in Szechuan, and the North China Plain, which by its record could scarcely claim to be stable in its yield but presumably merited inclusion by virtue of its importance in cotton cultivation .... It is noted that there is no mention of Heilungkiang in the discussion on policy on 'high and stable yield' areas ... perhaps because Heilungkiang had always enjoyed high priority (because of proximity to Peking) for agricultural producer goods .... Heilungkiang may have supplanted Szechuan as the largest grain exporting province (Donnithorne, 1970).

The situation described above, where the central Government provides investment grants and agricultural credit, may now have changed, following the delegation of responsibility to the provinces. The necessary funds for irrigation projects, hydro-electric schemes and agricultural mechanization are apparently now to be provided from the accumulated savings of the communes and counties.[2]

Forest Land

The relative success of re-forestation is important,

[2] See L.F. Goodstadt in *Far Eastern Economic Review*, 7 November 1970, pp. 14-17.

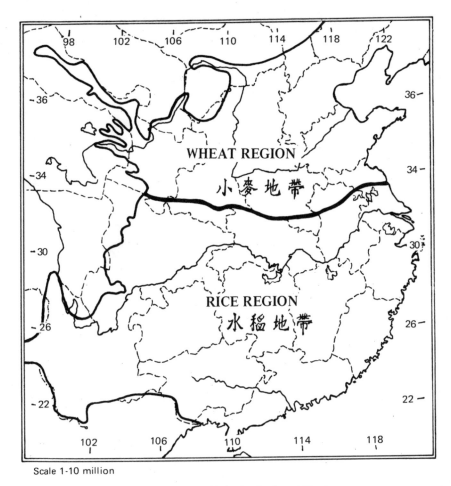

Scale 1-10 million

Fig. 2 The Two Main Agricultural Regions

since forest covers control water supplies for irrigation and reduce erosion. There have been unprecedented efforts in eastern China to plant trees, both for timber production and to conserve soil and water, but the percentage of failure has been appallingly high (Richardson, 1966). In the dry hilly areas, the ground cover of vegetation is less than 50 per cent. In many places, only 10 per cent of the trees planted have survived, because forest plantations are constantly ravaged by the rural people for fuel, and fire also takes a heavy toll. The demand for forest products will rise rapidly with increasing industrialization. The timber reserves of the residual primary forests are not likely to last more than twenty-five years; within that period, the current reforestation

schemes will yield little other than fuel, wood for pulp, and roundwood for local use.

But above all, the success of any irrigation project, the rate of siltation of reservoirs, and the initial control of rivers all depend in the final analysis on the state of the hill and mountain land higher up in the same catchment. There is therefore a direct correlation between forest management and food production.

Grasslands, Natural and Sown

A grassland and range ecologist could survey the grazing resources of the west, but this would be of little relevance to the food situation in the densely populated parts of eastern China. In the east, the genera and species of the Gramineae

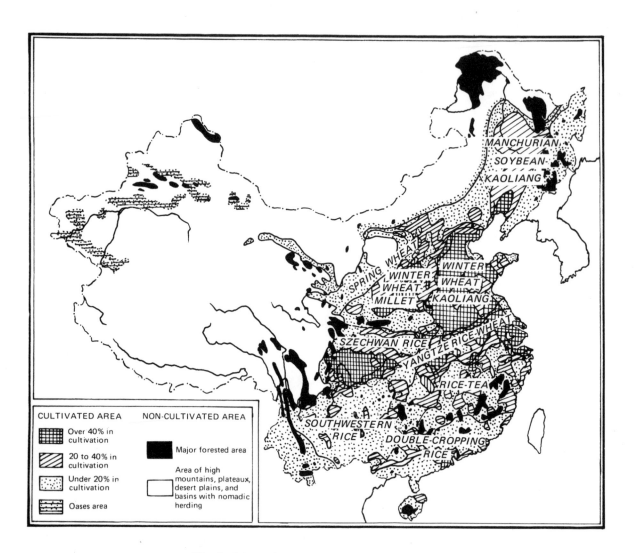

Fig. 3 Principal Land-use and Cropping Regions

characteristic of northern latitudes and a continental climate meet the subtropical genera and species that are characteristic of the monsoonal ecoclimate, extending along the southern Asian mainland from West Pakistan eastwards.[3]

Because of the great pressure on the cultivated land for food and cash crop production, and the broken and dissected nature of the terrain, it has to be assumed that pasture farming in crop rotations is out of the question. It does seem, how-

[3] For a list of the temperate and monsoonal grasses of China, see Whyte, 1968b.

ever, that more could be done in this type of country to develop a hill-slope type of cattle husbandry. A new system of land use could be evolved where water resources are available up the slope, where cattle sheds could be built on the slopes, and fodder grasses and legumes grown on terraces below the cattle sheds, irrigated with clean water or with the wash waters from the sheds that produce double the yield of feed.

Practical research in this labour-intensive system might be of great value in expanding the production of beef in a lactose-intolerant society,

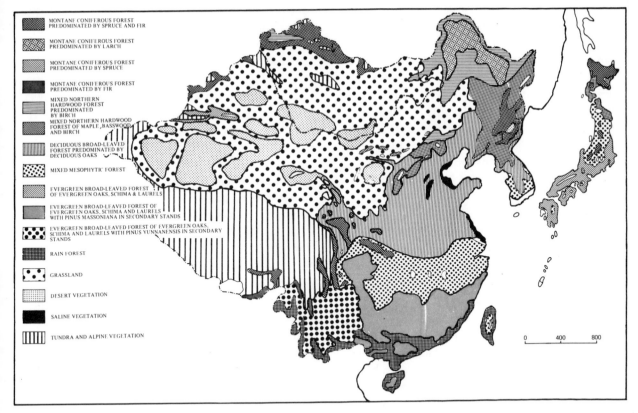

Fig. 4 Forest Types (now largely deforested), Semi-arid Grasslands, and other Types of Vegetation

where increased production of acceptable forms of animal protein (pigs and poultry) depends upon feeds grown on cultivated land, in competition with food and cash crops. The more expensive commodity, beef, could be produced for the higher-income urban groups, thus releasing more pig meat for the lower-income groups, as is being done in Japan.

Soil Types and Deficiencies

The soil types and their deficiencies may be summarized as follows:[4]

Wheat region:
lime-rich soils of grasslands, high fertility combined with low and variable rainfall;
chernozems of western Manchuria;
alluvial soils of Hwang Ho delta;
podzolic soils developed under moderate rainfall and former forest cover

Rice region:
highly leached, acidic, yellow-red soils associated with former tropical and sub-tropical forests

Those deficiencies noted in 1949 probably still apply, in view of shortage of artificial fertilizers:
15 to 25 per cent of fields potassium-deficient,
40 to 55 per cent phosphorus-deficient,
80 to 90 per cent nitrogen-deficient.

Fertilizers

Total requirements in 1970 have been said to equal 30 million metric tons;[5] availability in that year was 8.5 million metric tons, including the importation of 5 million tons. There is little doubt that most of these fertilizers would be reserved for the 'areas of high and stable yield', i.e. for the land producing industrial crops, or for the

[4] See 'The geography of mainland China: A concise sketch'. *Current Scene*, Hong Kong 7: 17 : 21 pp. and 4 maps. 1969.

[5] See 'The geography of mainland China: a concise sketch'. *Current Scene*, Hong Kong, 7: 17. 1 September, 1969.

best irrigated land on which foodgrains are produced in mechanized farming systems, for export to the urban centres or overseas (rice). It is very unlikely that scarce fertilizers can be spared for rural food production, including the private plots. These must continue to depend for renewal of soil fertility on the highly developed Chinese tradition of the use of organic manures. Stable manure in particular may be good for maintaining the structure and moisture-retentive capacity of the soil, but is relatively low in essential plant nutrients.

Most of the inorganic fertilizers are apparently nitrogenous. Soil specialists will probably agree that the minimum effective and economic rate of application for these, on good soils which have long been starved of essential plant nutrients, should not be less than, say, 300 or 200 kg. per hectare. For a calculation of the effects of 8.5 million metric tons on food production, it would be essential to know the relative allocations to the different soil types and crops, and to have an estimate of this maximum effective rate of application of single nutrients or balanced fertilizers under Chinese conditions.

Water Conservation, Flood Control and Extension of Irrigation

In the present context, one must consider whether these measures are greatly increasing the potential of the private plots or the production of crops used for production of animal protein. The index of multiple cropping stood at 140 to 145 per cent in the years 1956/8. It is known that great efforts are being made to reclaim cultivable and waste lands, and to increase the area under irrigation. It should not, however, be assumed that these new areas will immediately lead to a great increase in crop production. In many cases the land reclaimed and irrigated would be of low fertility; the addition of water alone, in the absence of heavy dressings of organic and inorganic fertilizers, and of some years of cultivation to produce a good tilth, cannot be expected to improve yields very markedly at once.

In assessing the implications for agriculture and food production of large water conservancy projects, it is necessary to know the purpose of the operation and its results in terms of gain or loss of cultivated land. The construction of reservoirs for town supply water or of drainage works to protect cities and other riverine communities against flooding may not increase the total or effective cropping area, and may even reduce it. Where projects of flood control are designed to protect existing cultivated land, one must know the former frequency of damaging floods (i.e. one in every two, five or ten years). In assessing the effects of irrigation projects on agricultural production, it is necessary to know whether the extra water will merely ensure stability of production in one season, or whether it can provide for production in a second season per year, where other growing conditions are favourable; also whether the land now to be irrigated has been cultivated already under a dry land system, or whether it is wasteland still to be reclaimed and levelled.

For example, in his study on water resource development in the Yangtze basin, Liang (1964, 1965) shows that, in the Three Cascades and the Two Cascades of the Yangtze, 43,000 and 184,000 ha. respectively of cultivated land had to be submerged in the construction of the reservoirs. Reference has been made in the press[6] to a massive water conservation project, the objective being the construction of a 150-mile long waterway through the Huaipei Plain in the Provinces of Honan, Anhwei and Kiangsu. This waterway is apparently primarily to protect the city of Tientsin from periodic flooding, which is most probably due to excessive run-off from the hill and mountain areas in the upper regions of the river catchment, deforested long ago. The project in the Huaipei Plain incidentally provides irrigation water for only 64,000 ha. of cultivated dry land and 12,000 ha. of reclaimable wasteland, but is also said to ensure protection of one million hectares of farm land from recurring floods.

During 1970 the New China News Agency has reported:

[6] *South China Morning Post*, Hong Kong, and *Hongkong Standard*, 7 July 1970, quoting from *China Reconstructs.*

(a) The Ouyang Hai irrigation system in Hunan, now providing irrigation for two-thirds (450,000 hectares) of the total planned area of the so-called bare-hand project;

(b) the enlargement of the irrigated acreage of Shensi by 200,000 hectares over the previous winter, thus doubling the 1958 area of irrigated farmland; and

(c) completion of an electric power/irrigation/drainage network in Sinkiang-Uighur rice-growing region, and the provision to the communes and production brigades of electric-power pumps, threshers, husking machines and presses and flour-mills.

Land Reclamation

Of the total land area, 12 per cent is now cultivated and 3 per cent cultivable wasteland, on which reclamation is a slow and costly process.

Plateaux of Production

Agricultural production over areas of cultivated land as vast as those of China does not progress by leaps and bounds. Claims for localized increases of 25 per cent or more must be regarded with suspicion, and certainly should not be extrapolated for application to whole regions. Having allowed for the marked climatic fluctuations characteristic of the monsoonal ecoclimate, it is usually found that increases in crop and livestock yields per annum or per decade are small. They proceed by steps, by means of improved agronomic practices, from one plateau to another, each successive step becoming more difficult and costly to achieve than the last. Each step has its own biological maximum, governed by environment, to which it may rise in relation to the economic inputs and human efforts which are applied. On rain-fed land without supplementary irrigation, successive plateaux may be achieved, first with maximum use of organic manures, second with optimal economic use of inorganic fertilizers, in both cases with improved but not yet high-yielding varieties. On second-class cropland depending upon rains in the wet monsoon season and irrigation in the dry, higher maxima may be achieved. On land with supplementary irrigation available through-

out the year, with fertile soils, optimal use of organic manures and inorganic fertilizers, plant protection and high-yielding varieties, the top and ultimate plateau of yield and production may be achieved, but the higher one climbs, the better must be the technological efficiency of the cultivators. In order correctly to assess national or regional claims for increased production, it would be desirable to know the number of hectares of land on each of these plateaux for all of the ecological regions or provinces of the country. Intensive animal husbandry in the monsoonal environment also demands a far higher standard of management, nutrition and disease control than is necessary in temperate countries.

Did the land of China cease to be able to maintain the people on a reasonable plane of nutrition as long ago as 1750 to 1775, when the population was 250 million (Ho, 1959)? It is stated that in 1578 there were 66 mou per family of total population. This was close to the figure regarded by early Chinese economists as adequate for a producing family (100 mou), since 80 per cent of all families were producers at that time. By 1729, there were only 35 mou per family of total population, so that the land had to produce nearly twice the yield (Ho, 1959). According to Teng (see Table 2), the present number of mou per producing family is 15 to 20, or five times the nutrition density of the eighteenth century.

Thus, since 1750, the state of equilibrium between the people and the land resources has deteriorated progressively (Hou, 1968; Dawson, 1966). It is one of the main objectives of the present Government to try to recover that equilibrium, by improved land use and farming practices and maximum reclamation of wasteland and extension of irrigation facilities, but with a human population over three times greater than that of 200 years ago. Recovery of equilibrium would be expressed primarily in the maintenance of good nutritional standards for non-rural peoples, while at the same time ensuring a great improvement in the standards of rural nutrition, particularly of the vulnerable groups.

Have yields of food crops per unit area reached a static level with the use of all available organic fertilizers? Hou Chi-ming (1968) refers to a continued low level of production in the post-1961 years, which has been variously ascribed to weather, the Great Leap Forward and the rural Communes. Hou considers rather that, during the most severe years of 1960-1, the food shortage in the rural areas might have been so serious as to inflict lasting damage to the health and physical strength of the peasants, and to reduce the number of draught animals considerably. All this should have resulted in a shortage of farm labour, due partly to the substitution of human labour for animal power. However, Hou finds no evidence to suggest such a shortage since 1960. He proposes that the agricultural set back may not be really a temporary slump, but rather that it reflects the basic stagnant nature of Chinese agriculture:

The apparent inability to break through the 1959 level of production, despite considerable increase in labour force, strongly suggests that an output ceiling may have been approached within the framework of traditional technology and inputs. Any significant increase in production may not be forthcoming unless modern inputs or new production functions are introduced.

High-yielding Varieties

It is currently fashionable to refer to the so-called high-yielding varieties of wheat and rice which have been associated with the 'green revolution' in some parts of Asia. These special synthetic products of plant breeders are quite different genetically from the improved strains and crossbred varieties of the past. China has been using the latter since at least the eleventh century. There is nothing to indicate that China has evolved or yet imported a true high-yielding variety of either rice or wheat. Her use of conventional improved strains is probably done on the advice of her plant breeders, who are well aware of the dangers of introducing high-yielding varieties into a country where both fertilizers and pesticides are in serious deficit.

Rural/urban Relations

Attempts to achieve maximum productivity by better farming practices, use of fertilizers and irrigation water are designed to increase procure-

ment from rural areas; the produce of the land, be it from the forests, the grasslands or the cultivated land, is intended for sale and consumption in urban and industrial areas, or for export to earn foreign exchange. In common with many Asian countries, China is stimulating maximum production by the great majority of the population for the benefit of a minority; the more efficient the extraction of food from the rural areas, the less diversified is the rural diet.

Donnithorne (1970) gives an account of the history and development of the tax and procurement system in relation to food grains and other crops. Tax is levied in respect of crops of all kinds —grains, potatoes, vegetables and industrial crops. The tax, which seems to vary between 4 and 19 per cent, is based on the normal yield of all crops reckoned in terms of the main grain crop of the area. The grain taken by the State in agricultural tax and the compulsory deliveries (the so-called 'commodity grain' as distinct from grain grown for home consumption) seems to vary around 23 to 34 per cent of total output in any one year. It would not, however, be correct to say that this represents the requisitioning of some 30 per cent of the crop for 15 per cent (the urban proportion) of the population. The State also needs grain to supply to the farmers otherwise engaged on the production of industrial crops.

Presumably because of limited production, the extraction of livestock produce from the rural areas is even more intense and efficient, since the rural diet is almost entirely vegetarian. Some of the incentives applied to induce the rural people to part with their pigs and other meats, eggs, etc. have been given by Myrdal (1966) (1961 data). Every goat delivered entitles one to coupons for 6 chi of cotton material or one sheepskin or goatskin. When pigs, goats or eggs are sold to the State, the household receives, as well as cash payment, permits to buy:

| for one goat | six chi[7] of cotton material or one goatskin or sheepskin |
| one pig | one set of cotton under- |

[7] Chi (tsin in Cantonese). 10 chi = 1.333 oz.

TABLE 3. Prices Paid by the State for Animal Products sold Privately in 1962

	yuan per jin[1]
pigs, liveweight	0.43
goats, liveweight	0.43
eggs	0.795

Source: Myrdal, 1966

TABLE 4.   Prices Paid by the Grain Office in Yenan Hsien in 1962

	Yuan per jin
Wheat	0.10
Millet	0.06
Millet , 'sticky millet'	0.065
Maize	0.065
Black beans (*Vicia faba*)	0.08
Soybean	0.08
Long beans (*Phaseolus vulgaris*)	0.075
Green beans (*Phaseolus mungo*)	0.10
Buckwheat	0.065
Kaoliang	0.065
Hemp seeds	0.15

Source: Myrdal, 1966
[1] jin ('kan' in Cantonese)   1 jin (kan) = 1.333 lb.

clothes *and* one pair of galoshes *and* one or two hand towels

one jin of eggs   half a jin of sugar

Examples of the prices paid to rural people are given in tables 3 and 4.

Intensification of Agriculture

In Asia, the more primitive types of land use or farming systems are frequently associated with a better opportunity to obtain a balanced diet than exists in areas of more intensive crop husbandry. Protein malnutrition is likely to have occurred increasingly with the spread of settled agriculture, as forests became inaccessible or their fringes depopulated of traditionally hunted fauna. This deterioration in the rural diet will have occurred earlier in the now more densely populated countries. Relatively primitive peoples, including the tribals living in remote highland areas near relict forests, are able to diversify their diets by hunting, collection of insects, edible vegetable foods and horticulture. On intermediate slopes without irrigation (where there is still a soil cover), the farmer may have different types of land within his holding and be obliged to grow different cereals and other crops; these improve his diet, particularly if he is far from markets. When one reaches the irrigated plains, all the land is farmed in large units on an intensive system to one or more of the major crops for commune subsistence and export from the rural areas. Here the rural diet must be monotonous and unbalanced. Thus there is an inverse correlation between intensification of agriculture and diversification of the diet.

III
Ecoclimate or Agroclimate

AN ecoclimate is the natural climate of any given environment. An agroclimate is the environment where the crops grow, an ecoclimate modified by man by the provision of irrigation water, by the growing of shelterbelts, and by changing the soil environment with the application of fertilizers and the improvement of its water retentive capacity. An ecoclimatic basis for a nutritional assessment may be obtained from a map of climatic regions and climatic types (Fig. 7).

The chief climatic controls are those of the winter and summer monsoons. Most of the population of China lives in a monsoonal ecoclimate which is part of the vast region geographers throughout the world call Monsoon Asia. Huang Ping-wei (1961) states that 46 per cent of the area of China is in the Eastern Monsoon Sector, 27.3 per cent is Mongolia-Sinkiang Highlands (part of the Eurasian steppe-desert zone), and 26.7 per cent is the Chinghai-Tibetan Highlands. The Eastern Monsoon Sector is broken down further into areas, sub-areas and zones.

The Chinese ecoclimate is not a separate entity, but part of an Asian zone which is only now coming to be studied and interpreted as an ecological unit, with great local diversity in terms of land use, crop and animal husbandry, and standards of human nutrition. It must be remembered that the word 'monsoon' does not refer, as is popularly believed, to a marked seasonal wet season, but is derived from an Arabic word meaning a seasonal wind. Thus one has wet and dry monsoons, depending on season of the year and passage over the sea. Until the meteorologists can define the monsoonal ecoclimate more precisely, we must conclude that Monsoon Asia stretches over the mainland of Asia from West Pakistan to Korea, and including the insular countries along the western Pacific (Japan, Taiwan, Philippines and Indonesia). Much of China comes within the influence of the Pacific summer monsoons, and

probably some 70 to 80 per cent of the population lives in provinces affected thereby.

Chang Jen-Hu (1971) has summarized the work of the Academia Sinica on the analysis of the general features of the upper air circulation in east Asia. The nature of the mean circulation over the whole of Monsoon Asia in January and July is shown in Figs. 5 and 6 (Wu Hung-shun and Chen Lung-shun, 1956; and Dao Shih-yen and Chen Lung-shun, 1957, reproduced in Chang Jen-Hu (1971). According to Chang, it is most important to realize that the monsoon circulation is a far more complex and far less self-contained system than the classical concept of differential heating between land and ocean had led us to believe; for the westerlies that form the basic current in the greater part of China are part of the hemispheric circumpolar vortex.

It should be noted, however, that these maps do not precisely indicate the agroclimatic characteristics of Monsoon Asia. This would require a separate study, and would probably produce a picture of roughly latitudinal zones extending from the Equator to the temperate and continental climates to the north of Monsoon Asia. The actual conditions within these zones would, of course, be greatly influenced by the factors of altitude and exposure to the monsoonal winds.

Careful consideration must be given to climatic fluctuations. The history of rural China is a history of disasters (Mallory, 1926) (Tables 5 and 6). Flood prevention and river control may have modified the picture to some extent. But droughts cannot be controlled. Provided climatic data are available for a sufficient number of years and from enough recording stations, one may calculate drought expectancy for the different ecological regions. There is no evidence that this has yet been done for China. It is essential for the planning of agriculture and the storage of food reserves at strategic points.

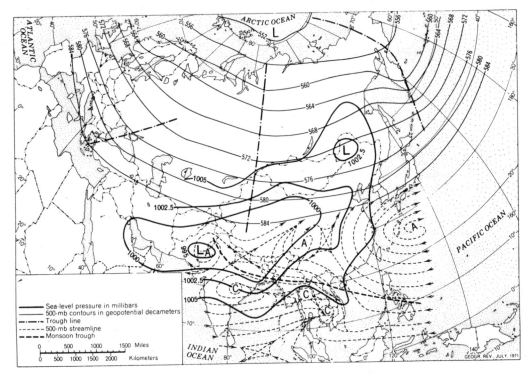

Fig. 5 Asia: Mean Circulation in January

Fig. 6 Asia: Mean Circulation in July

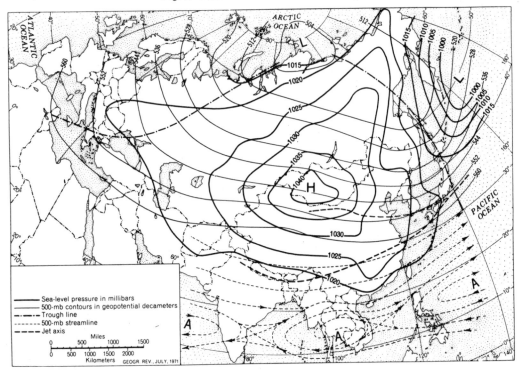

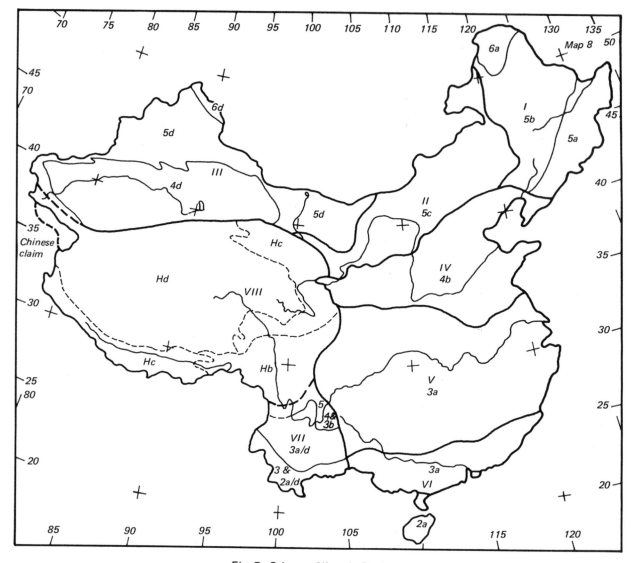

Fig. 7 Primary Climatic Regions

Primary Climatic Regions

Eight Primary Regions	Climatic Types[3]	Warmth[4]	Dryness[5]
I NORTHEAST	6a/–/–/–/–	Cold temperate	Wet
	5a/5b/–/–/–	Temperate	Wet/Semi-wet
II INNER MONGOLIA	–/–/5c/–/–	Temperate	Semi-dry
III KANSU-SINKIANG	–/–/–/6d/–	Cold temperate	Dry
	–/–/–/5d/–	Temperate	Dry
	–/–/–/4d/–	Warm temperate	Dry
IV NORTH CHINA	–/4b/–/–/–	Warm temperate	Semi-wet
V CENTRAL CHINA	3a/–/–/–/–	Subtropical	Wet

VI SOUTH CHINA	3a/–/–/–/–	Subtropical	Wet
	2a/–/–/–/–	Tropical	Wet
VII EASTERN TIBET [SIKANG]-YUNNAN	–/5b/–/–/–	Temperate	Semi-wet
	–/4b/–/–/–	Warm temperate	Semi-wet
	3a/3b/–/–/3a/d	Subtropical	Wet/Semi-wet
	–/–/–/–/2a/d	Tropical	Wet s., dry w.
VIII TSINGHAI-TIBET	–/Hb/Hc/Hd/–	Cool to cold	Semi-wet/semi-dry/dry

1) The division is that of a 1959 scheme prepared for the Committee on Delimitation of Natural Regions of the Chinese Academy of Science by Chang Pao-k'un, Chu Kang-k'un, et. al.

2) West-to-east divisions are based on indices of relative dryness; south-to-north divisions are based on temperature zones. The eight primary and 31 secondary regions (omitting the 32nd, the South China Sea) comprise 20 climatic types, most of which are shown on the map.

3) Combinations of warmth and dryness are shown by number-letter notation. Numbered zones, for China, are all monsoonal. Letter H, for Tsinghai-Tibet, indicates non-monsoonal, plateau-type climate.

4) Stated as the sum of daily mean temperatures (°C.) for duration of active growing season (≥10° C.) as follows:

1	Equatorial	about		$9000°$
2	Tropical		$\geq$	$8000°$
3	Subtropical	$4500°$	–	$8000°$
4	Warm temperate	$3400°$	–	$4500°$
5	Temperate	$1600°$	–	$3400°$
6	Cold temperate		$<$	$1600°$

5) Stated as the ratio of potential evaporation to precipitation. Authors postulate equilibrium (=1.0) for zone of Chinling Shan and Huai River.

	$<$ 0.50–*Very Wet*; water drains
a	0.50-0.99–*Wet*; water drains
b	1.00-1.49–*Semi-wet*; deficiency of water
c	1.50-4.00–*Semi-dry*; irrigation is needed
d	$>$ 4.00–*Dry*
a/d	*Wet* in Summer, *Dry* in Winter

TABLE 5.   Number of Droughts per Century
during Different Dynasties

DYNASTY	TANG	FIFTH DYNASTY AND NORTH SUNG	SOUTH SUNG	YUEN	MING	MANCHU
Christian Era	*618 - 907*	*908 - 1126*	*1127-1279*	*1280 - 1367*	*1368 - 1643*	*1644 - 1847 1861 - 1900*
Capital	*Chang-an Shensi*	*Kai-fung Honan*	*Hangchow Chekiang*	*Peking Chihli*	*Peking Chihli*	*Peking Chihli*
Honan	4.2	17.8	1.3	34.4	2.2	26.0
Chihli	2.1	6.9	3.9	25.3	1.8	43.7
Shensi	9.1	1.8	3.9	4.6	2.2	11.6
Shansi	0.7	2.3	–	4.6	7.3	12.3
Shantung	1.7	5.5	0.7	20.7	2.2	27.7
Kansu	0.3	1.8	1.3	5.7	–	8.3
Chekiang	1.4	1.4	17.8	4.6	4.0	22.7
Kiangsu	1.4	2.7	9.9	3.4	1.5	43.8
Hupeh	0.3	0.9	4.6	4.6	0.7	26.2
Szechwan	0.7	–	2.6	–	1.1	2.9
Anhwei	0.7	3.7	5.9	4.6	–	36.3
Kiangsi	0.7	1.4	5.9	4.6	1.5	21.8
Hunan	–	1.4	–	3.4	1.1	20.6
Fukien	–	0.9	4.6	4.6	3.3	6.5
Kwangsi	–	0.5	–	1.2	0.7	1.6
Yunnan	–	–	–	–	6.9	2.5
Kweichow	–	–	–	–	–	2.5
Kwangtung	–	0.5	0.7	2.3	1.5	7.0

Source: Mallory, 1926

TABLE 6.   Number of Floods per Century
during Different Dynasties

DYNASTY	TANG	FIFTH DYNASTY AND NORTH SUNG	SOUTH SUNG	YUEN	MING	MANCHU
Christian Era	*618 - 907*	*908 - 1126*	*1127 - 1279*	*1280 - 1367*	*1368 - 1643*	*1644 - 1847 1861 - 1900*
Capital	*Chang-an Shensi*	*Kai-fung Honan*	*Hangchow Chekiang*	*Peking Chihli*	*Peking Chihli*	*Peking Chihli*
Honan	4.2	24.2	5.3	21.9	2.9	12.4
Chihli	2.1	9.1	9.9	29.9	5.1	26.9
Shensi	4.5	6.9	5.3	12.7	7.3	9.5
Shansi	4.5	2.3	5.3	19.6	13.8	7.3
Shantung	3.4	3.7	6.6	8.1	4.0	19.0
Kansu	0.4	1.4	0.7	5.8	0.7	7.0
Chekiang	3.1	4.1	15.2	6.9	16.7	13.9
Kiangsu	4.2	4.1	14.5	10.4	3.3	15.7
Hupeh	1.7	2.3	4.6	12.7	16.0	11.2
Szechwan	1.7	–	9.2	2.3	1.5	0.4
Anhwei	4.5	7.8	9.9	4.6	2.2	14.5
Kiangsi	1.7	0.9	6.6	3.5	4.4	13.6
Hunan	1.7	2.7	4.0	6.9	5.1	8.7
Fukien	1.4	1.4	5.9	4.6	7.6	3.7
Kwangsi	–	0.5	–	6.9	4.7	2.1
Yunnan	–	–	–	–	6.5	0.8
Kweichow	–	–	–	–	1.1	–
Kwangtung	–	–	1.3	4.6	2.9	0.8

Source: Mallory, 1926

IV
Population

NEITHER Peking nor anyone else knows the size of the population of Communist China. Ironically, this lack of population data may be more frustrating to the non-Chinese analyst who is constantly searching for figures in order to construct economic indexes and to make political and social prognostications than to the Chinese themselves, who are well aware of the existing population pressures but are not overly concerned with the precision or timeliness of the statistics available to measure them (Orleans, 1969).

Data on total population in 1950, 1960 and 1965 are published in the U.N. *Demographic Yearbook,* the U.N. *Monthly Bulletin of Statis-* *tics* and U.N. *World Population Prospects.* In the past, the U.N. calculations depended on the somewhat inadequate data reported by the countries. In 1967, the U.N. began to publish its own estimates, but only for selected countries, and for the years since 1958. On these bases, the Food and Agriculture Organization of the United Nations, for its own purposes, carries out evaluations in order to establish the most plausible figures for its own work.[1] The U.N. estimates for 1950

[1] Personal communication from the Director, Statistics Division, Food and Agriculture Organization of the United Nations, August 1969.

TABLE 7.   Population According to Different Estimates (in millions)

Sources	Percentage annual increase, compound	1950	1953 Census Year	1955	1958	1960	1965	1970
China (official)[1]	1.6		575	602	647	667	700	780[a]
United Nations[2]	1.6	560				650	700	760
FAO[3]	2.0	547				686	764	845
US Bureau of Census[4]			578/576	599/703	637/650	662/682	715/743	770/805[a]
Chou En-lai[5]	2.0					667		
	2.5						744	848
Orleans[6]	1.6	567	589	608	640	658	705	757
Chandrasekhar[7]	2.2	552	588	614	662	690	769	858[a]
Frisen[8]								760

[a] Figures for 1970 estimated on basis of earlier years and percentage annual increase.

Sources: [1] Field (1962)
[2] United Nations (see footnote 1).
[3] Food and Agriculture Organization (see footnote 1).
[4] Aird (1968)
[5] Hou (1968)
[6] Orleans (1969)
[7] Chandrasekhar (1967)
[8] K. Frisen, at Conference of International Planned Parenthood Federation, Tokyo, October, 1970, quoted by Snyder (1970).

and 1960 appear to the FAO statisticians to have been based on available official data for China, and to have been considerably rounded to reflect uncertainties in them. Figures for the later years appear to have been obtained by applying a constant annual increment of 10 million. This applies an annual rate of growth of around 1.5 per cent compound, which appears low as compared with the rate of growth implied by the official Chinese estimates of total population and of birth and death rates available for 1952-7, and quoted in the U.N. *World Population Prospects*. The estimates used in FAO are based on the 1953 Population Census and the rate of growth of around 2 per cent implied by the official country estimates, and corresponding to the high variant of the U.N. *World Population Prospects*. No substantial reduction in the rate of growth has been assumed for recent years in view of the absence of any reports of success for family planning campaigns.

Various estimates of the population of China are summarized in Table 7. For the calculation of food resources and requirements, it is appropriate to take the figure for 1970 of 800 million ± 6 per cent; and further, to say that 80 per cent or 640 million, again ± 6 per cent, are rural people (some authorities say 85 per cent).

Figures for annual rate of growth of population (Table 7, column 1) are relevant to projections for agricultural planning, regulation of food exports and imports, and a preliminary estimate of the sequence of events in a future crisis, should population outstrip actual and potential sources of food. The latest figures of 1.1 per cent per annum quoted by Snyder (1970) would seem to savour of competition between the provinces in achieving the national target of 1 per cent per annum, now that they have been delegated the responsibility for population census.

V
Rural Health

ALL these estimates of population are, of course, strongly influenced by the controlling factors of infant mortality, deaths of children up to 10 years of age and maternal mortality, and by the degree of success of improved sanitation and other public health measures[1] in reducing rural disease and overall death rates. The availability of qualified medical personnel has a bearing on the extent and efficacy of curative medicine and the control of maternal mortality, and, of course, on the spread of knowledge of satisfactory nutrition. There are no data to assess the rural impact of these factors.

The efforts of the present regime to improve rural health by raising the standard of cleanliness in villages and consequently reducing the presence of the disease carriers are well-known. There are heroic tales of whole communities being mobilized to rid an area of both crop pests and carriers of human diseases. A substantial drop in the death rate has been claimed, although no reliable statistical evidence has been produced. Undoubtedly even mechanical measures will bring about a temporary improvement. Intestinal, respiratory and other diseases transmitted by contact with the sick, by unclean water, rodents, snails, mosquitoes, cockroaches, flies, sandflies, larvae and ticks all, however, require regular medical attention to cure the infected, and repeated use of chemical pesticides to eliminate the vectors. There is a critical shortage in China of doctors, of medicines and of pesticides.

In 1966, there were 100,000 doctors trained in modern medicine, capable of advising on the prevention and cure of endemic tropical diseases and familiar with nutritional deficiencies.[2] Mao Tse-tung said in 1965 that 85 per cent of the farm-ing people had not had access either to doctors or to medicines for many years. The proposal to move 50 per cent of trained medical personnel to the rural areas, even if wholly successful, can have little impact on a population of 640 million. Moreover, since the Cultural Revolution all education, including that of medical students, has been disastrously disrupted. It is too early yet to evaluate the new, 'practical' curricula of re-opened universities, to which students with inadequate secondary education are being admitted.

The travelling barefoot doctors, who receive brief training in simple first aid and preventive measures, may achieve a greater impact if they are available in sufficient numbers to cover the vast areas and populations involved, and if they are provided with adequate medicines and chemicals. There are not, however, enough fully trained doctors on call in rural areas to be able to advise the barefoot doctors on less elementary matters, as is the case with para-medical staff in other Asian countries. The barefoot doctors are also being entrusted with the spread of birth control measures.

Malaria has not yet been conquered in large areas of Asia, even after intensive, costly, long-term campaigns, where facilities in the form of spraying equipment, chemicals, transport and trained personnel were available (Sandosham, 1969). Limited success has been achieved in South-East Asia with the elimination of filariasis (of which there are two varieties in China), by carefully controlled, regular use of prophylactics in an attempt to reduce the rates of transmission. This requires considerable organization, supervision by trained staff, and adequate supplies of diethylcarbamazine. There have been recurrent claims that the schistosomiases found extensively in the Yangtze basin and south-eastern China have been eliminated (Adams, 1964, Bowers, 1970). However, no biological means of control have yet

---

[1] See 'Public health developments—continued focus on the farms'. *Current Scene*, Hong Kong, 7:24. 15 December, 1969.
[2] Ibid.

been discovered; the various methods tried so far, including pathogenic bacteria, competing snails and predatory fish have all proved unsatisfactory.[3] It is obviously impossible to remove by hand all snail hosts from all the watercourses in areas of rice monoculture. Again, neither the qualified personnel nor supplies of sodium antimonyl tartrate, the most effective remedy, are available to cope with curing the seriously affected, and with the widespread administration of prophylactics to those living in endemic areas, many of whom may be affected without knowing it. The worm may live up to twenty years in the human host.

Water supplies are easily contaminated by faecal material, both from humans and animals, by seepage during the wet monsoon, and by dust during the dry. Myrdal (1968) has noted that, throughout Asia, the incidence of water-borne diseases (cholera, typhoid, dysentery, diarrhoea and intestinal parasites) is very high, and protected water supplies rare. Apart from cholera, these diseases are rarely fatal to the adult, but they sap vitality and adversely affect labour inputs and efficiency. The cure of these diseases depends on adequacy of medicines and of doctors to administer them. This also applies to the common Asian diseases of tuberculosis (as prevalent in rural areas as in cities), pneumonia and bronchitis, characteristic of overcrowded and ill-ventilated housing, especially sleeping arrangements.

Nutritionists generally find that Asian peoples do not often boil water drawn from wells or other sources for drinking. The Chinese are perhaps unusual in boiling their drinking water, if fuel is available and if there is time. However it is children who like to play in and around ponds, puddles and streams, who are most prone to various infections, and who will pass these on to the rest of the community. Chinese children wear trousers with an open seam instead of a gusset, enabling them to squat and relieve themselves without adult assistance. Mothers in a north Shensi village said that bladder disease was common until children went to school and could be supervised (Myrdal, 1966). Children are particularly vulnerable to helminthic infestation. In September 1970, the Provincial Health Department, Taiwan, found three out of every four school children to be affected. The average rate of infestation for the whole population of much of Asia is about 80 per cent, usually with more than one variety of intestinal worm.

All these factors have a bearing on infant mortality, adult morbidity and population increase. They both exacerbate and are exacerbated by malnutrition.

[3] Personal communication, Professor P.F. Basch, Department of Community and Preventive Medicine, Stanford University School of Medicine, California, U.S.A. 27 August 1970.

VI
Diet in Rural Areas

THE history of rural nutrition is closely related to the history of agricultural production. It is known that two major changes took place in early times. From the fourth to the first centuries B.C., the increase of population and the decrease of land available for pasturage caused the Chinese to limit greatly their meat intake, and to change from consumption of beef and mutton to that of pork and dog-meat. From this time on, cattle were used mainly for draught, and milk and milk products disappeared from the diet. A second important change took place between the third and sixth centuries A.D., when rice replaced wheat and pulses as the staple in the south. Vegetables and fish compensated for the reduced mineral, vitamin and protein content of the diet consequent upon this change (Ho, 1959).

In a country in which agricultural production is so subject to regional ecoclimates and seasonal or annual variations in rainfall and temperature, it is essential to recognize the parallel responses in terms of rural diets. These are largely dependent upon seasonality of production, especially of perishable foods that cannot be stored for use in off-seasons. This is a fact that has not always been taken into account in generalizations about the dietary patterns and standards, particularly by foreign visitors who see what the markets are selling or what the people are eating in one season only. A dietary survey should record food availability and consumption in all seasons of the year, probably in four seasons in the temperate/continental north of China and in three seasons in the monsoonal southern provinces. The survey should also be repeated over a five-year period, so as to record the effect of annual fluctuations in climate. Few surveys up to this standard of accuracy have been conducted anywhere in Asia. Ideally, crop and livestock specialists should be members of any such team.

An excellent example of a nutritional survey covering different seasons of the year is available from Tamil Nadu State, India (Sundararaj, Begum, Jesudian and Pereira, 1969). The survey was confined to pre-school children. Statistically significant differences were found in protein intake; this was 2.07 gm. per kg. of body weight during the rainy season, when groundnuts and freshwater fish were available, and only 1.46 gm. per kg. body weight during the cold season. Fat provided 14 per cent of daily energy intake during the rainy season, again due to groundnuts, but only 4 to 6 per cent for the rest of the year. Seasonal differences in the intakes of vitamin A, riboflavin and vitamin C were also found. Clinical signs of both vitamin A and riboflavin deficiency appeared during the cold season. A report from China during the early 1950s noted that there was a higher incidence of beri-beri during the month of June, probably due to the length of time rice had been stored before consumption (Hueck, 1952).

An indication of the effect of seasonality is shown in birth weights of full-term infants in west China (Lee, 1948). Despite severe deprivation of essential foods over the preceding eight years, there was little variation in birth weight over the eight years of study, but there was a marked seasonal variation. Infants born in January were heaviest and infants born in September of each year were the lowest in weight. These differences were undoubtedly related to seasonal availability of foods.

The only study of rural nutrition on a country-wide basis in China is that made in the survey organized by J. Lossing Buck from 1929 to 1933 of 22 provinces, 16,786 farms, 38,256 families, in 186 localities (Buck, 1937). Dietary standards and practices were reviewed by Maynard and Wenyuh Swen (1937). The agroclimatic and cropping regions which were recognized after that survey are shown in an adapted form in Fig. 3. The distribution of production of the major

TABLE 8.   **Income and Food Consumption of Categories of Rural People, 1955**

	Total	Members agric. prod. co-ops.	Poor peasants	Middle peasants	Rich peasants	Previous landlords
Average income per household (yuan)	692.9	704.6	488.7	774.4	1297.0	497.2
Average expenditure	667.7	702.3	473.3	743.2	1272.2	497.1
Consumption per head in kg. per annum:						
Foodgrains	186	195	196	189	207	180
Meat	4.6	4.65	3.7	4.9	5.7	3.55

Source: Chen, 1966.

foodgrains may be taken as the basis of the rural dietary patterns. The diet of a farm family consisted then, as it does now, largely of foods produced on their own land, supplemented by purchases, foraging and gifts. The proportion of food supplied by the farm varied widely in different regions, and was lowest where a valuable cash crop was grown.

In terms of the contribution of foods to calorie intake, 83 per cent came from foodgrains, 9 per cent from grain legumes and vegetable oils, (but a high proportion of the carbohydrate in soybean is indigestible (FAO, 1967)), 4 per cent from sweet potatoes, not more than 1 per cent from vegetables, and 2.3 per cent from animal products, including pork 1.3, lard 0.4, and the remainder from beef, mutton, chicken, duck, fish and eggs; there were then approximately 8 eggs available per male adult equivalent per year. The total calorie intake per day in the rice region was 3,186, 66 per cent provided by rice; in the wheat region, 3,295, with (per cent) contributions: millet 25, wheat 25, kaoliang 14, maize 11 (see Table 10 for recommended calorie intakes).

Thus the rural diet was then, as it is now, predominantly vegetarian, with the usual disadvantage of bulk representing a strain on the digestive organs and favouring the onset of intestinal disease. The daily per caput protein intake recommended at that time was 70 gm.; this was exceeded in all areas surveyed, particularly in the wheat area. Concern was, however, expressed at the high proportion of vegetable protein (70 per cent from foodgrains), which was considered particularly undesirable for children. Consumption of animal protein was nowhere sufficient to be of nutritional significance. Children were at the greatest disadvantage, especially since such protein as was available was treated as a luxury, and was not divided among the family according to physiological need (Maynard and Swen, 1937).

Calcium was everywhere deficient; this led to a deficiency of phosphorus, and was probably aggravated by a deficiency of vitamin D. This may have been partially offset by exposure to sunlight, although children spent much time inside dark dwellings or within high-walled courtyards. Intake of vitamin A was thought to be inadequate, except in the double-crop rice area where sweet potato was regularly consumed. It was doubtful whether vitamin C was adequate, although scurvy was not observed. Vitamin B and iron were probably deficient in some areas.

In 1955, a sample survey was conducted by the State Statistical Bureau, covering 16,000 peasant households in 25 provinces (Table 8).

There are other fragmentary indications of rural diet. In 1954, in Kansu, the annual consumption of foodgrains was 223.8 kg. per head, and in 1956, 238.6 kg.; meat consumption in 1954 was 1.76 kg. and in 1956, 2.62 kg. per head. Rich peasants in Hunan had 6.5 kg. meat per head per year,

TABLE 9. Comparison of Food Consumption between Urban and Rural Areas, 1957,
(from countrywide study by State Statistical Bureau)
(in kg. per head per year)

	Urban	Rural
Foodgrains	200	216
Edible oil	6.4	1.9
Meat	7.0	3.85
Sugar and candy	3.85	0.85

Source: Chen, 1966.

middle peasants 4.7 kg., and poor peasants 3.0 kg. (Chen, 1966). Karnow (1968) interviewed a peasant from Kwangtung in 1962; he said the ration was 200 gm. rice per meal, with meat at New Year and Ch'ing Ming. Peasants could grow their own vegetables, and buy some meat on the free market. Reporting on a visit to a commune west of Peking in 1967, it was said that the evening meal regularly consisted of 'thick noodles in meat gravy, heavy bread and a communal bowl of fried vegetables' (Hunt, 1968).

A week's menu in August 1962, in a village in northern Shensi was based on the following. Breakfast usually consisted of millet porridge, with either turnips, pumpkin or fried beans, tomatoes and potatoes, and watered gruel. The mid-day meal staple was steamed millet, maize porridge, millet bread, bean flour and wheat noodles or steamed potato cakes, with vegetables and their water as soup. Vegetables were beans, tomatoes, turnips or cabbage. The last meal of the day was invariably millet porridge, occasionally with steamed pumpkin or maize cobs, since the maize had just been harvested. Onion, garlic and chilli added flavour to meals. No animal protein of any kind appeared in the week's menu. Meat was eaten four or five times a year (Myrdal, 1966).

Japanese families returning to Japan in 1970 after thirty years in Heilungkiang said that in the Paohsing People's Commune in Fangcheng Prefecture, each working peasant received 150 kg. grain a year, enough to feed a family for four months, and an average of one yuan (about 50 U.S. cents) per day with which to provide the remainder of the grain, supplements and all family necessities.

Sorghum, maize, millets, rice, wheat, soybeans and vegetables were cultivated, but rice was a treat reserved for New Year's Day; they could afford meat, in the form of Chinese ravioli, only three or four times a year. People were hungry most of the time because there was not enough to eat.[1]

How far is it possible that patterns of food production and diets have changed in rural areas since the 1930's? Buck's survey showed that 90 per cent of the small individual holdings was used for the production of the principal foodgrain or other cash crops, ten per cent for the supplementary subsistence cereal grains, and for soybean, sweet potato, rapeseed, broad beans, peanuts, green manure, green mung beans, field peas and vegetables, according to region. These areas of 10 per cent of the cultivated land thus provided foodgrains for subsistence, crops for sale or to provide relish to the staple food, and feed for animals. A high percentage of quality foods was sold for cash (soybean 30; cabbage 50; egg plant 52; other legumes 20). A further proportion of the remaining legumes was used for feed and seed. The use of soybeans in the rural diet has been greatly exaggerated. In Buck's survey, soybean appeared in only 38 to 39 per cent of diets, and then only in insignificant amounts.

[1] Life in a Red Chinese Commune'. *Japan Times*, 7 August 1970. Further detailed and local information comes from anthropological studies, such as Diamond (1969); Fei (1939); Fukutake (1967); Hsu (1949); Lin (1948); Wolf (1968); Yang C.K. (1959); and Yang, M.C. (1945). Recent observations from travellers relate primarily to urban areas or reflect the special hospitality accorded during officially organized trips to Communes.

Today it is claimed that 5 per cent of the total cultivated area is regarded as private plots, the allocation to individual families varying according to numbers. Doubtless a similar range of crops is grown. Out of reach of the large towns, it is possible that the rural market for vegetables has diminished. Specialist horticulturists farm only near large urban markets; traditional rural vegetables, in season, are those of least nutritive value: the pumpkins, gourds, cucumbers, melons and Chinese cabbage (Wolff, 1962). The question is whether as much of today's production from the private plots is sold as was sold thirty years ago. If so, the diet must be quantitatively even more deficient in respect of quality foods than that of the smallholders studied by Buck, although it is probably superior to that of the landless thirty years ago.

Animals in China are reared for draught, to provide organic manure, and as a cash crop for urban areas and for export overseas. Meat and fish are purchased in very small amounts for festivals. Eggs are rarely eaten on the farm. Efficiency of control and compulsory disposal to the State, together with illegal private transactions, probably ensure that extraction of livestock products from the rural areas is at least as effective as it was thirty years ago.

Two fundamental factors cannot have changed greatly—the pattern of production of the major crops, and the dietary habits and preferences of the population. Two major changes have, however, occurred. Local harvest crises are mitigated by foodgrain loans from the Central Government. Improved access has made possible greater efficiency of extraction of food for urban areas. This applies to foodgrains, and to foods of plant and animal origin rich in high-quality protein, vitamins and minerals. It appears, however, that the State procurement plan meets with considerable resistance, especially during periods of political upheaval or local climatic crises. During the Cultural Revolution, some rural producers not only shared much of their crops among themselves, but even raided stores in which State buffer stocks were maintained.

It is no doubt national policy that the rural peoples should grow quality foods on their private plots to diversify their diets. However, the incentive for the farmer is not better nutrition for his family, but production of a marketable commodity. In the years before 1956, prices offered by the Marketing Co-operatives were so low that many subsidiary crops were abandoned. A free market was re-established in 1956 for vegetables, fish, poultry products, etc., a small, perhaps sub-standard proportion of which would be reserved for the home. During the period 1961-4, the commune system was largely abandoned, and the village once more became the administrative unit (Wenmohs, 1967). Each family was again given a private plot, its size depending on the number in the family. Private production of poultry for home use and for sale was encouraged. While the increase in grain output during this period was largely due to better weather, some credit must also be given to the increased energy and enthusiasm of the rural cultivators. Since 1966, however, private plots and subsidiary production have come into increasing political disfavour, being said by Peking to lead to 'spontaneous capitalism' (Wenmohs, 1967). Their future is therefore uncertain.

Thus three factors—reduction in the size of private plots, increased efficiency of extraction of all foods from rural areas, and the natural inclination of the Chinese farmers to sell produce for cash—are obstacles to the improvement of the rural diet with quality protein and vitamins. This is of particular significance in the correct nutrition of the vulnerable groups.

VII

Chinese Dietary Traditions

THE Chinese humoral beliefs, deriving both from Ayurvedic theories which entered China with Buddhism, and from the Chinese theory of the Yin and the Yang, oppositeness and complimentarity, which evolved during the third century B.C., have greatly influenced beliefs regarding health and nutrition. Sickness (unless caused by supernatural agency) occurs when the bodily elements are unbalanced, and may be cured by the use of medicines and foods possessing the opposite character; consequently water and cooling herbs are used to cure 'fire' (inflammation or infection). Similar beliefs occur throughout Asia (Whyte, 1972).

The Taoists in particular concentrated special attention on the inner cause of illness, which they saw as an improper balance between the Yin and the Yang. They considered that a correct regimen in all seasons prevented illness. The importance of a complete and balanced diet was fully recognized in the medical classics of the Han period, one of which advises:

Taking the five cereals as nutriment, the five fruits as assistants, the five meats as chief benefactors, and the five vegetables as supplements, and combining together the *chii* and the tastes in the diet; this blending is what benefits the mind and the body (Needham and Lu, 1962).

Ancient texts from the fourth century B.C. to the second century A.D. differ with regard to the five grains, mainly according to latitude.[1] Thus these are either: wheat, glutinous panicled millet (sorghum), panicled millet, beans and hemp; or wheat, rice, panicled millet, beans and hemp. The most ancient medical classic, which Needham and his associates think dates from about the second century B.C., lists wheat, rice, yellow millet, beans and soybean, while Buddhist texts of the third or fourth century A.D. quote wheat, rice, hemp, barley and mung bean. It would appear that some

ambiguity exists between the terms 'grains' and 'cereals' as translated from Chinese texts. In modern parlance, the soybean and the mung bean would qualify (with the other edible grain legumes or pulses) as grains, along with the cereal food-grains, but not as cereals. Hemp would not appear to belong under either head.

Needham states that the five fruits are: peach, plum, apricot, chestnut and jujube (*Zizyphus jujuba*); the five vegetables: mallows, wild leeks, shallots, small onions and a variety of chive; the five meats: beef, mutton or goat meat, pork, dog-meat and poultry.[2]

The ancient theories regarding diet and health have percolated into folk tradition in the form of a basic sense of the importance of balance in the diet, strongly influenced by common lore regarding the heating or cooling properties of foods. As in other Asian countries, opinions on the individual foods vary from one region of China to another. This concept of balance, together with beliefs regarding the strengthening properties of animal protein foods, seems to have prevented the development of the injurious dietary taboos which affect the vulnerable groups of the Indian subcontinent and South-East Asia. The dietary injunctions of the major religions are, of course, irrelevant in China today; it appears doubtful that they ever affected large numbers of the lay population, though Chinese Moslems observed the taboo on pork.

The ancient counsel against eating uncooked food or food contaminated by rodents or insects (Needham and Lu, 1962), if adhered to, certainly helps to reduce disease.

There is general agreement that during pregnancy and nursing, cooling foods are dangerous; unfortunately this includes most fruits and vegetables, though mango is considered heating. Birth

[1] Personal communication, Dr. Joseph Needham. 25 November 1970.

[2] As for note 1.

itself is heating, and so is breast milk; the infant is fed barley water or rice flour gruel to compensate this. Several nutritious foods are valued by the Chinese mother. Meat is recommended both during pregnancy and lactation. It was in the past considered essential for the nursing mother to eat a precisely defined number of eggs, of chicken and of fish (Jelliffe, 1968), but only middle-class and wealthy mothers could afford these. It is unlikely that family budgets in China today will permit the regular use of such luxuries, even when locally available, or that the mother alone would take enough of them. Pork fat and red gram, cuttlefish soup, shrimps' heads in wine and a special wine of glutinous rice together with blow-fly larvae have been mentioned as galactagogues in the north, while Cantonese mothers coming from rural areas in Kwangtung will make a soup of fish heads, peanuts and papaya.[3] It must be remembered that all these recommendations are not —indeed cannot be—carried out in practice with sufficient regularity to meet physiological requirements, because of their cost, limited availability, and because the Chinese woman today does not have much time for complex preparations for herself alone.

In China, as elsewhere in Asia, weaning has traditionally been a gradual process, a supplement of congee being introduced in the first weeks of life. Denial of the breast takes place usually well after the first year, frequently not until the second, or when a subsequent pregnancy intervenes. With Cantonese women this is done abruptly, over a single day, since it is believed that milk not drawn from the breast deteriorates and is bad for the baby.[4] Congee is cooked for two hours together with bits of liver, pork or fish, which are removed before feeding the child.[5] Soybean products are little used; the Cantonese mother, probably influenced by their colour, believes that they cause anaemia. In the north, vegetable soup may be mixed with the rice before the child is one year old. After the first year, different soups and egg are given, if available. These practices are similar to those of southern Chinese peoples in the countries of South-East Asia today. The fruit of *Zizyphus jujuba* is mashed and given to the child, as it is believed to form blood. In Shensi, mothers breastfeed until the child is two or three years old. At seven months, a thin porridge of millet, rice and water is introduced; this is followed by a gruel of millet and water alone. The gruel is thickened at one year, and subsequently noodles and steam-baked bread are given. Vegetables and egg are given only after the child is completely weaned at three years, since it is believed that they cannot be digested before that age.

[3] Dr. Marjorie Topley concluded in 1970 a survey of child rearing practices and beliefs about illness among ten families from resettlement estates and ten families from low-cost housing units in Hong Kong. The majority of mothers came from rural areas in Kwangtung. Dr. Topley's findings will be published by the Centre of Asian Studies, University of Hong Kong. A preliminary outline was given at the Child Development Centre, Yaumati, Kowloon in 1970.

[4] As for note 3.

[5] Information provided by Dr. Flora Baber, Child Development Centre, Hong Kong. A study has been carried out by Professor C.E. Field of the Department of Paediatrics, University of Hong Kong, and Dr. Baber, to obtain standards of growth and development of Chinese children in Hong Kong, correlating these to social environment. A preliminary report will be published in 1972, while the statistical material, covering the first three years of life of the children studied, will appear later. The study will be continued until the children are five years old.

VIII
The Vulnerable Groups

THERE are four critical phases in the early life of the human organism: from conception to birth; from birth to weaning; from weaning to about six years of age; and adolescence. Inadequate nutrition at any or all of these phases is expressed in impaired growth, reduced resistance to disease in the short-term, and sub-normal physical growth in the long term. Inadequate nutrition during the first three phases may result in impaired neuro-motor development in the short term, and reduced mental capacity in the long term. Defective nutrition of the mother during pregnancy has deleterious effects on the growth and development of the offspring, which cannot subsequently be remedied by a satisfactory diet for the infant.

The vulnerable groups of a population require proportionately greater amounts of certain nutrients than are necessary for an average healthy adult. Additional calories are required during pregnancy and lactation, but there is little evidence that the rural mother does, or is able to increase her total food consumption. The FAO/WHO Expert Group on Protein Requirements (FAO, 1965) recommends additional high-quality protein: 6 gm. per head per day during the latter half of pregnancy, and 15 gm. during lactation. Requirements of some vitamins and minerals are also higher. Poor maternal diets are the cause of low birth weights and high foetal and infant mortality. Milk secretion does not normally fall unless there is gross deficiency in the maternal diet; sustained production may be achieved at the expense of the mother. Diets are likely to be deficient in vitamin A, the B complex and ascorbic acid, all, particularly the water-soluble vitamins, reflected in the breast milk. Protein and calcium in breast milk generally remain constant, being furnished from maternal reserves when deficient. Nutritional anaemia is a universal Asian problem, particularly associated with rice diets, aggravated by inadequate protein for globin synthesis and hae-morrhages due to high hookworm infestation.

Where the mother is healthy, breast milk is adequate until the child is about six months of age; then supplements of calories, vitamins, minerals and proteins are essential for the child, increasing until final weaning, when some type of animal protein is important. WHO (1969) recommends supplementation from three or four months, but Jelliffe (1968) considers the risk of infection from the supplements before 6 months too great to warrant this.

It can be seen from Chapters VII, X and XI that inadequate amounts of good quality protein, vitamins and minerals are consumed in pregnancy or lactation. This is confirmed from biochemical findings with Chinese mothers in Malaysia, whose blood samples taken at birth of the infant show low serum protein and low serum vitamin A (Thomson, Ruiz and Bakar, 1964).

Some informants say that the crêche system has been adopted largely for the infants of factory workers in China, and that arrangements in most rural areas are more informal, the old women looking after the children while the mothers are in the fields. The duration of breast-feeding—that is how long the mother is able to carry her infant on her back while working—is crucial, since it is very unlikely that adequate animal protein (and consequently vitamins and minerals also) can be provided during her absence.

Adequate supplies of good quality protein, minerals and vitamins are necessary for growth from weaning throughout childhood, with increased requirements during adolescence. Again, there is no information on the composition of school meals on which to base an assessment of their adequacy. In view of the overall lack of legume and animal protein (see Chapters X and XI) and of the low availability of vegetables per caput, it is, however, unlikely that children's needs throughout their growth are fully met.

IX
Principal Sources of Calories

In China, as elsewhere in Asia, carbohydrates are the principal source of calories. China's staples are shown in Fig. 3. A map of the distribution of crops is a direct indication of the plant foods which are the basis of rural diets. Rice is the staple of over 70 per cent of the people, particularly in the southern monsoonal provinces. Wheat and kaoliang are the staples in the north. Maize is not popular, and is largely reserved for livestock feed. It is, however, eaten by the mountain-dwelling peoples (mostly non-Han), who also consume buckwheat, other cereals and roots and tubers, depending on environment. In China, as throughout the region, sweet potato is a low-prestige food; it is frequently denied that the rural peoples of the south are still obliged, as they were in the past, to supplement their rice supplies with this staple (see however Chapter XI).

The first requirement of any policy designed to feed a population is the provision of calories. It is obvious that the Government is fully aware of the overriding need to provide at least a minimum quantity of foodgrains for all the population, urban and rural (Table 10). Foodgrain sup-

TABLE 10. Recommended Calorie Intakes, revised December 1962

Male adults, weight 60 kg.	Calories per day
Very light labour	2,400
Light labour	2,600
Medium labour	3,000
Heavy labour	3,600
Very heavy labour	4,200
Female adults, weight 50 kg.	
Very light labour	2,200
Light labour	2,400
Medium labour	2,800
Heavy labour	3,400
Pregnant, after 5th month	300 +
Nursing	1,000 +
Young male, weight 54 kg., 16 to 19 years	3,000
Boy, weight 42 kg., 13 to 16 years	2,600
Young female, weight 50 kg., 16 to 19 years	2,700
Girl, weight 42 kg., 12 to 16 years	2,500
Children, male and female	
10 to 13 years	2,300
7 to 10	2,000
5 to 7	1,600
3 to 5	1,400
2 to 3	1,200
1 to 2	1,100
Under 1 year	100 per kg. bodyweight
Under 6 months	120 per kg. bodyweight

Source: Compiled by China Medical Science Academy, Research Institute for Labour Health, Environment Health and Nutrition Health, (1963).

plies are ensured by procurement from the rural areas after the needs of the farming population have been considered, plus import of wheat, primarily for the great cities of the north. Regional variations in availability in the rural areas due to climatic fluctuations or other causes are covered by temporary allocations on loan from State buffer stocks. There is considerable discussion regarding the actual level of foodgrain harvests in recent years (Field, 1968; Swamy and Burki, 1970).[1]

China exports fine-quality rice to Cuba, Ceylon, Pakistan, Hong Kong, Malaysia, Singapore and Japan. Every ton of rice exported is roughly equivalent in cash value to two tons of wheat imported (Table 12). Press reports in September 1970 show that rice exports have fallen by 250,000 tons. This may be due to increased demand from a larger population, increased rural resistance to procurement, or lower production.

[1] The Bank of Japan (*Japan Times*, 9 July 1970), places cereal output in 1969 at 190 million tons, only 5 million tons up from 1957; this means that the cereal production (unprocessed) per caput dropped from 282 kg. per year for a population of 656 million, to 256 kg. per year, assuming a 1969 population of 730 million. Donnithorne (1970) (see Chapter II) places total output in 1967 at 190 million tons, or 253 kg. per head per annum for a population of 750 million. Klatt (1970), believes that only in the years following the Great Leap Forward were less than 210 kg. grain available per head per annum, and that during 1970 the figure may have been 'slightly higher'.

TABLE 11.   Grain Areas, Yields and Production[1]

	Average[2] 1953/7	1962	1963	1964	1965	1966	1967	1968 (prel.)
Rice[3]								
Area (thous. ha.)	30,354	29,300	28,200	29,500	29,800	30,000	29,500	29,500
Yield (kg./ha.)	2,566	2,750	2,780	2,880	2,920	2,740	2,930	2,780
Production (thousand metric tons)	77,870	80,600	78,400	85,000	87,000	82,200	86,400	82,000
Wheat								
Area	26,831	24,400	24,200	25,500	25,000	24,500	24,500	24,500
Yield	840	870	900	1,000	900	850	940	860
Production	22,610	21,200	21,800	25,500	22,500	20,800	23,000	21,000
Miscellaneous grain								
Area	51,585	52,000	53,000	53,000	53,500	53,000	53,500	54,000
Yield	1,102	1,050	1,030	1,055	990	1,000	1,055	1,040
Production	52,190	54,600	54,600	56,000	53,000	53,000	56,500	56,000
Potato								
Area	10,067	13,100	13,300	12,500	12,500	12,500	13,000	12,500
Yield	1,906	1,800	1,775	1,880	1,800	1,760	1,850	1,840
Production[4]	19,260	23,600	23,600	23,500	22,500	22,000	24,000	23,000
Total								
Area (million ha.)	118.8	118.8	118.5	120.5	120.8	120.0	120.5	120.5
Yield	1,448	1,515	1,502	1,577	1,531	1,483	1,578	1,510
Production (million metric tons)	172	180	178	190	185	178	190	182

Source: [1] U.S. Consulate, Hong Kong (Washenko, 1969).

[2] *The Great Years*, Foreign Languages Press, Peking, 1960.

[3] in terms of paddy rice.

[4] converted to grain equivalent—4 units of potatoes equals 1 of grain

TABLE 12. Imports and Exports of Foodgrains in China, 1967-70
(in 1,000 metric tons)

	1967	1968	1969	1970
Wheat imports	4,133	4,329	4,600	4,500 (contracted up to September)
	1959	1963	1966	1967
Rice exports	1,700	513	1,150	1,000

Source: Fats and Oils Division, Foreign Agricultural Service, U.S.D.A. and
         U.S. Department of Commerce, provided by U.S. Consulate, Hongkong, May 1970

X
Sources of Plant Protein

THE value of protein from different foods may be expressed in percentage protein content, or, more significantly, in biological value. Biological value is the proportion of absorbed nitrogen from food retained in the human body for maintenance and/or growth (Table 13). Biological value is governed by the content of and proportion between essential amino acids. Protein is composed of a number of amino acids, some of which cannot be synthesized by the human body, and which must be present simultaneously in the diet. These are termed the essential amino acids. If any one of these is deficient in a meal, utilization of the total protein consumed is diminished in direct proportion to the deficit. Most animal proteins contain sufficient proportions of the essential amino acids to ensure a high percentage of protein utilization in digestion. Plant proteins are deficient in one or more of the essential amino acids to such a degree that a considerable proportion of ingested protein is unavailable in digestion. In particular, cereal grains are deficient above all in lysine and marginally deficient in methionine, and grain legumes in methionine.

To ensure maximum production and availability of proteins from foodgrains, the following steps must be taken:

(a) Introduction of high-yielding varieties so that the total production and thus protein yield per hectare on the best land is increased. China had an earlier generation of improved varieties, but has not yet begun to use China-bred or introduced I.R.R.I. (International Rice Research Institute) types of the so-called high-yielding varieties of rice, which have been associated with the green revolution elsewhere in Asia.

(b) Screening of all existing varieties within China to assess protein content of the grain. Work elsewhere in Asia indicates that there is a wide variation within the existing genetic material.

(c) In a diet relying almost entirely for its protein upon foodgrains, it is the amino acid content and proportion which is the important factor. Therefore screening of existing varieties has to be undertaken also for amino acid content. The technique of biochemical analysis has still to be perfected, being subject to considerable margin of error (F.A.O., 1970). There is no reason to doubt that the breeders in China are fully aware of this approach.

(d) If protein needs cannot be met from conventional foodgrains eaten alone or in association with appropriate grain legumes, it has become customary to consider fortification, i.e. the addition of natural or synthetic materials providing the deficient components. Fortification can be achieved by the addition of protein isolates, based on milk or various legumes. This, however, cannot be contemplated in China since it would involve greatly increased production from the land.

There is no evidence that the production of single-cell protein has passed the experimental stage anywhere in Asia.

A cheap means of improving the value of plant proteins is fortification with synthetic amino acids. So far, only lysine has been manufactured anywhere on an economic scale. The considerable problems of fortification of subsistence crops have to be overcome. Moreover, studies on the nutritive value of lysine-fortified cereals at five centres in India have shown benefit from lysine supplementations of wheat diets, but not of rice diets. Further, lysine supplementation of both wheat and rice diets confers no significant benefit where such diets are already deficient in calories, vitamins and minerals (Indian Council of Medical Research, 1969).

TABLE 13.   The Protein Content and Quality of Protein in Foods

	Protein percentage in edible portion		Protein content gm./100 calories	Biological value	
Ideal protein				100	
Egg (hen)	12.4	13 to 13.5	7.5	96	100
Egg (duck)	13.0	16.5			
Meat (muscle)		20.6		80	
Beef (lean)	17.5		9.6		80
Pork	12.0	16.65			84
Fish, fatty sea	20.0[1]		11.4		83
" tilapia	17.5				
" medium cured fatty	40.0		15.3		
Milk, (cow, fresh)	3.5	3.31	5.4		75
" (cow, skimmed)	36.0		10.0		
" (powdered whole)	26.0				
" (sweetened condensed)	8.1	8.8			
" (unsweetened condensed)		35.6			
" (evaporated whole)	7.0				
Milk (buffalo)	5.8				
Soybean (grain)	38.5	39.85	11.3	75	
Soybean (fresh in pod)		19.5			
Soybean (sprouted)	6.2	11.5			
Other grain legumes	20 to 30	20 to 30	6.4	40 to 50	47
Rice (home-pounded)	7.1		2.0		
Rice (highly milled)	6.7				
Cooked rice		3.38		70	67
Congee (rice gruel)		0.81			
Wheat (grain or wholemeal)	10.5	12.4			
Wheat (flour)	8.6	10.8	3.3		52
Kaoliang	10.1	9.5 to 11			
Millet (*Setaria italica*)		9.59			
Millet (unspecified)		2.9 to 3.4			56
Maize (wholemeal)	9.5	7.7 to 9.2	2.6	55	56
Taro (*Colocasia*)	1.9	1.10	1.7		
Sweet Potato	0.6 to 1.3	1.08	1.1		

Sources: Column 1, World Health Organization, 1969
    "   2, Ch'en and Li, n.d.[2]
    "   3, Brock and Autret, 1952; Davidson and Passmore, 1966
    "   4, Food and Agriculture Organization, 1965
    "   5, Davidson and Passmore, 1966[2]

[1] There is wide variation in per cent edible portion and protein content among different species of fish.

[2] See also: F.A.O. (1949); F.A.O. (1954); U.S. Department of Agriculture (1952); Her Majesty's Stationery Office (1962); Ang (1960); F.A.O. (1969a).

Before discussing the soybean in particular as a source of plant protein, one must refer to the relative value of diets based on foodgrains plus grain legumes in terms of amino-acid balance. In cereal grains other than millets, lysine is the first limiting essential amino acid, while methionine is marginally deficient. In grain legumes there is ample lysine, but a deficiency of methionine. Nutritionists throughout the world have shown that a diet based on a judicious mixture of plant proteins is equal in value to a diet containing animal protein. What is not always realized, however, is that, with the possible exception at a certain time of the year in northern India, nowhere in Asia are grain legumes available or consumed in quantities sufficient to ensure this desirable balance.

In China, a satisfactory diet could theoretically be obtained by means of the soybean, by far the most valuable grain legume in protein content. FAO (Aykroyd and Doughty, 1964) has given the following amounts and combinations as representing a satisfactory diet. In a child's diet of 1,100 calories per day, 30 gm. soybean with wheat or 45 gm. soybean with other foodgrains provides adequate protein. In an adult's diet of 2,200 calories per day, 30 gm. soybean is adequate with all foodgrains. However, only with wheat is 90 gm. soybean per day sufficient for a pregnant or nursing mother; even this large amount is inadequate with a rice diet; 90 gm. of any legume other than soybean in combination with Chinese staples cannot provide an adequate diet for a nursing or pregnant mother. The total consumption of soybean and other legume nowhere approaches these required quantities.

In 1959, the total exports of soybean and soybean oil from China were nearly 1.6 million metric tons, including 1,528,064 metric tons of soybean, and 50,800 metric tons of soybean oil. Some authorities suggest that since then the area under soybeans has fallen from about 10 million hectares to 8.5 million hectares, but this does not appear to have affected exports of soybean from China (Table 14).

It is generally assumed that the rural people obtain soybean from their private plots. However, when one compares resources of soybean in relation to requirements, the situation is highly revealing (Table 15). If we are to provide an average of 40 to 50 gm. soybean per head per day for the total rural population of 640 million (this average takes into account the different requirements for soybean of different sections of the population), this would mean that the whole of the private plot area (assuming that they are and remain at 5 per cent of the total effective cultivated area) would have to be sown to edible varieties of soybean, and that the yield per hectare would have to be *double* that obtained in the larger units, where oil-producing varieties of soybeans are grown for industrial purposes or for export. Yields on private plots are likely to be lower than on the large-scale units, because they are usually located on poorer soils and fertilizers are not allocated to their owners.

TABLE 14.   Value of Exports of Soybeans from China 1959 - 67.

Year	Value (US $1,000)
1959	49,455
1960	59,522
1961	30,269
1962	33,710
1963	34,328
1964	53,635
1965	67,175
1966	67,700
1967	68,239

Source: U.S. Department of Commerce, provided by U.S. Consulate, Hongkong, May 1970.

TABLE 15.   Soybeans as a Source of Plant Protein: Nutritional Targets for
Total and Rural Population at Different Levels of Intake
(expressed in terms of the land areas required to produce them)

Population (million)	Soybean intakes at three levels (gm. per head per day)		Total amounts required per year (kg.)	Average yield per year [1] (kg./ha.)	Total approximate area of land required under edible varieties (hectares)[2]
800 (total)	(a)	30	8,760,000,000		12,500,000
	(b)	40	11,680,000,000	700	16,700,000
	(c)	50	14,600,000,000		21,000,000
640 (rural)	(a)	30	7,008,000,000		10,010,000[3]
	(b)	40	9,344,000,000	700	13,330,000[3]
	(c)	50	11,680,000,000		16,700,000[3]

(a)   provides adequate protein in an adult diet
(b) and (c) are higher levels to cover the requirements of total adult population with additional amounts to meet the special needs of the vulnerable groups.
[1] F.A.O., 1967.
[2] existing area about 8.5 million hectares, mostly under industrial varieties
[3] mostly to be grown on private plots.

Source: Compiled by the author.

There are other factors which reduce the value of protein from vegetable sources. One is the loss of protein which occurs in processing. The total content of rice grain is ± 8 per cent. Cooked polished rice contains only 3.38 per cent protein (Table 13). Mature soybeans containing nearly 40 per cent protein are available in the rural areas for only a limited period of the year. The protein content of the rest of the plant, consumed green throughout growth, is much lower (Table 13). Again, the method of preparation of grain legumes has an important bearing on the degree to which they may be absorbed in digestion. When finely ground, protein absorption in digestion is high. The most common method of preparation on the farm is simple boiling. Intestinal absorption is much lower than with, for example, soybean curd or soybean milk, consumed mostly in urban areas, although soybean curd is a traditional New Year dish. Moreover, with both curd and milk, the percentage of protein in the total edible portion is relatively low, varying according to the method of production; soybean milk contains an average 3 per cent protein, while that of curd varies from 8 to 12 per cent. Individual servings are small. Intestinal diseases and infestations reduce still further the amount of absorption of plant protein. Soybean sauce, that ubiquitous ingredient of the Chinese diet, is of insignificant value as a source of protein (FAO, 1966).

XI
Sources of Animal Protein

Pigs

FROM 1949 to 1959, the pig population varied from 57 million to 180 million. Subsequent to 1959, it fell to a lower figure, and has not yet regained the 1959 maximum. For ease of calculation, we may take the figure of 160 million.[1] The annual slaughter from such a population, taking Taiwan figures as the basis (Table 16), would be 84 million pigs (Whyte, 1970), lower than the percentage usually quoted for China. The average dressed weight at slaughter, based on the average of nearly 2 million pigs imported per year into Hong Kong from China, is 50 kg.[2] Thus the amount of pig meat available per annum for the total population of China, urban and rural, is 5 kg. per head. This compares with figures for Singapore, Taiwan and Hong Kong respectively of 11, 16 and 25 kg. of pig meat per head per annum.

Most of the pigs produced in mainland China are purchased for the urban people, confirming the vegetarian nature of the rural diet. There is no uniform system for rationing of pork in Chinese cities. When supplies are plentiful, pork is freely sold, but in times of scarcity, it may be rationed for periods of several months at a time.

If sweet potato vines and tubers are used in pig rations in China to the extent reported for Taiwan, one million pigs will consume 0.5 million tons of this feed. If the 8 million hectares under sweet potato in China give the average Taiwan yield of 16 tons per hectare, the Chinese production is 128 million tons per annum. A population of 160 million pigs in China consuming sweet potato at the Taiwan rate would require 80 million tons. Presumably the remaining 48 million tons is used as human food. If this could be replaced in human diets by a superior staple (see Table 13), the pig population could be increased by 50 per cent, to 240 million. But to achieve the levels of consumption of pig meat in the other Chinese Asian communities such as Singapore, Taiwan and Hong Kong, China itself would need 340, 500 or 800 million pigs respectively, calling for a production of 170, 250 or 400 million tons of sweet potato from 10, 15 and 25 million hectares of land, plus the other essential grain, and concentrate feeds already in short supply, with perhaps saccharified crop residues.

Poultry

Most of the chickens and ducks are kept in the monsoonal environment south of the Tsinling. There is no evidence to suggest that breeding and feeding are being given any more attention in China than in the past, and losses from disease are heavy.[3] Figures of poultry population and production for the year 1952 (almost unchanged from those of 1933) show the infinitesimal contribution of these excellent sources of animal protein to the rural diet in China; most meat and eggs are sold to urban areas (Table 17). The availability of about eighteen eggs per person per year is similar to the figure for India, but these national average figures are, of course, meaningless in relation to rural nutrition.

Let us try to modernize the duck industry of China to provide 50 eggs per person per year, one per week instead of one every 4 months. We may consider the Ng Chow and Pekin breeds in the New Territories of Hong Kong (Table 18), maintained on an intermediate level of husbandry.

Other Domestic Livestock and Fish

The use of beef and milk is insignificant in the rural diet; there is probably a potential for much

---

[1] The technique of calculating human nutritional targets in terms of livestock numbers, feed requirements and land area needed was evolved by Whyte and Mathur (1968).
[2] Information provided by Agriculture and Fisheries Department, Hong Kong.
[3] The mathematics of breeding and feeding poultry to meet human nutritional targets will be discussed by Whyte in *The Land of Monsoon Asia* (in preparation).

TABLE 16.   The Mathematics of Pig Breeding and Feeding
(Taiwan: planning pig production to meet targets in human nutrition)

A.   Requirement for pig meat

Year	Human population (million)	Actual and anticipated consumption per head per annum (kg.)	Total annual production to meet these targets (metric tons)
1965	13.0	14.48	188,709
1966	13.3	14.76	196,973
1967	13.6	15.08	205,223
1968	13.9	15.45	214,523
1969	14.1	15.85	224,119
1970	14.4	16.29	234,446

B.   Livestock population required to achieve these targets

Year	Total number of pigs to be slaughtered a year[1] (million)	Sows required to maintain this production	Boars per year	Total pig population (million)	Growing animals (million)
1965	2.7	206,200	2800	5.5	2.8
1966	2.9	217,250	2750	5.7	2.9
1967	3.0	229,300	2700	6.0	3.1
1968	3.2	242,350	2700	6.2	3.3
1969	3.4	256,400	2650	6.5	3.5
1970	3.6	270,450	2550	6.8	3.7

[1] Average slaughter weight, six to ten months old: total liveweight 90 kg.; meat 63 kg.

C.   Supply and Demand of Livestock Feeds in Taiwan in 1968 (metric tons)

Feedstuff	Local production	Available for Feed	Requirement for Feed	Shortage
Rice bran	244,960	244,960	256,302	11,342
Sweet potato	3,795,000	3,219,309	3,219,309	—
Wheat bran	8,450	8,450	89,013	80,563
Maize	96,000	86,700	207,356	120,656
Sorghum	20,400	18,400	18,400	—
Soybean	91,800	—	211,300	211,300
Peanut oil meal	45,500	45,500	69,778	24,278
Rapeseed oil meal	27,300	27,300	20,220	—

D.   Areas of Cropland Required

Crop	1965 Plant Area Ha.	1965 Harvested Area	1966 Plant Area Ha.	1966 Harvested Area
Sweet potato	234,145	234,060	235,567	235,443
Wheat	11,119	11,119	14,507	14,356
Maize	18,704	18,615	22,328	22,220
Soybean	53,176	53,156	51,326	51,323
Peanut	103,642	103,621	98,244	98,026
Rapeseed	17,593	17,593	17,783	17,679
Sorghum	4,101	4,090	5,102	5,100

Source: Thomas Yu, Joint Commission for Rural Reconstruction, Taipei.

TABLE 17. Egg Output in Relation to Human Population

	Total birds (millions)	No. in lay (millions)	Annual lay per bird	Total eggs (millions)	Eggs per head of human population per year
Chickens	265	132.5	90	11,925	15
Ducks	64	32	80	2,560	3.2
Geese	10	5	70	350	0.44

Source: Figures for total egg production from Liu and Yeh, 1965.
(Egg availability calculated for 1970 population.)

increased beef production (Chapter II). Goats are reared in the north, but mutton consumption is largely confined to the non-Han pastoralists of the grasslands of the north and west.

Similar calculations could be made for hens, if it were planned to raise egg and chicken meat production above the level of farm scavenging on a large scale. As with the pig and duck rearing industries, there is little doubt that Chinese breeders and farmers could greatly improve the genetic quality of their poultry stocks and reduce the losses from disease. It is, however, in the matter of the feed resources needed for a larger and more demanding animal population that the major difficulties arise, and will become more acute as competition with human population for the same foods intensifies.

Conclusion

Animal feeds and fodders must also be found for the draught animals working in the fields, oxen in both north and south, buffalo (12 to 13 million) for the paddy fields, mostly south of the Tsinling line. These livestock, however, make a negligible contribution to the resources of animal protein for the human diet, especially in the rural areas.

It must be expected, however, that, as in the rest of Asia, animal husbandry is in retreat in the face of the inexorable demand for land for the production of food for direct human consumption. F.A.O. has advised its member countries of Asia and the Far East (which do not yet include China) to concentrate their limited resources on pig and poultry production, because these types of livestock are the most efficient converters of feeds and fodders. This is a debatable policy for a country like China, if the pig and poultry industries are to be dependent on the cereal grains and sweet potatoes that might be used for human

TABLE 18. Calculations for Provision of 50 Duck Eggs per Head per Year for 800 Million People, using Chinese Breeds[1]

Breed	Duck eggs per head of human population per year	Total eggs required for 800 m. (millions)	Eggs produced per bird per year	Ducks required in lay (millions)	Total duck population required (millions)	Feed required Per bird per annum (kg.)	Feed required For total duck population per annum (thousand metric tons)
Ng Chow	50	40,000	180	220	440	47	2,068
Pekin	50	40,000	150	266	532	56	2,979

Source: Based on data provided by Agriculture and Fisheries Department, Hong Kong.

[1] If we are to consider the meat-producing capacities of these breeds, one may calculate on the basis of:
Ng Chow: 2.5 kg. liveweight at 9 weeks on 7.3 kg. feed
Pekin: 3.1 kg. liveweight at 9 weeks on 10.4 kg. feed.

food. In the case of the relatively unacceptable sweet potato, the land might have to be transferred to production of a foodgrain, cereal or leguminous.

So much for the production of animal protein from the land. According to F.A.O. statistics, China is the fourth fishing nation in the world in terms of annual catch. None the less, fish, fresh or dried, does not appear to play a regular and significant part in the diet of rural peoples, other than those living near coasts, along important watercourses or on lake sides.

Despite the great obstacles to the expansion of the production of animal protein from the land, neither in China nor in any other Asian country can a defeatist outlook be accepted. With the technical knowledge at our disposal, it is still possible greatly to increase the quantity and to improve the quality of the animal food which is produced. It is, however, vital that a greater proportion of this animal protein be retained in the rural areas, and channelled to the diets of those whose need is greatest—the pregnant and nursing mothers and the children after weaning.

XII
Status of Rural Nutrition

J.K. Galbraith has said:

... a poor peasant society, whatever it calls itself, is subject to the same cruel parameters of over-population, insufficient land, insufficient capital, insufficient education, and a technology that is limited by all these .... Circumstance, if sufficiently obdurate and compelling, leaves little opening for ideological preference.[1]

We are considering the ecology of nutrition of 640 million people ± 6 per cent; that is, 20 per cent of the world's population. Their calorie requirements are ensured by State intervention when necessary. They are expected to obtain quality and diversity in the diet mainly from their private plots. If these are actually 5 per cent of the total effective cultivated area, this means that the rural peoples have at their disposal 7.5 million hectares for the cultivation of their protective foods.

Animal protein in nutritionally effective amounts disappeared long ago from the rural Chinese diet. It would appear that the amount of protein available from grain legumes, especially the soybean, is also completely inadequate. Vegetables of relatively low nutritive value are consumed in small amounts, and supply is subject to wide fluctuation in seasonal availability, with deficits in winter in the wheat zone, or the dry monsoon period in the rice zone. Thus foodgrains are expected to provide not only the bulk of the calories, but also most of the protein, to the extent that their composition of essential amino acids permits (Table 19).

Nutritional recommendations contain a margin of safety, designed to protect the majority of a population, taking into account both differences in weight and height, and efficiency of utilization of foods. It is difficult, in view of wide variations between human beings, to determine a minimal

[1] J.K. Galbraith, 'It's lucky men don't control events'. Article in *The Washington Post,* quoted in *Ceres* 3:2, p. 15 (1970). No date for original article given.

effective intake of essential nutrients. This is even more true of children, since development takes place at different ages under different conditions of environment and nutritional status. It has been stressed (Yeh, 1959) that no standard can reasonably be set up for the whole of China on account of these differences. Recommendations must therefore be treated with caution when used as a yardstick to assess the adequacy of existing diets, or when recommending improvements. It appears likely that the average rural Asian, provided he is healthy, and despite heavy intestinal infestation, may be able to subsist on a diet in which the protein, and also some minerals and vitamins, are considerably below recommended levels.

In attempting to assess the status of rural nutrition in China, however, and even after allowance has been made for this adaptation to a lower plane of nutrition, it is obvious that there are severe deficiencies in important foods and nutrients, and that the vulnerable groups of the population are most at risk. When the present and potential production and consumption of animal foods, grain legumes and vegetables are related to the ratio of cultivated land per head of population (nutrition density per unit area), it is difficult to see how the rural Chinese diet can be improved on the scale required. If, in future, the private plots are destined to disappear and efforts become concentrated on increasing production of foodgrains to feed an ever-increasing population, the rural people will continue in that nutritional half-life which is so characteristic of Monsoon Asia. Until we have reliable evidence to the contrary, it would appear correct to assume that nutrition and medical specialists would be able to recognize the evidence of malnutrition in general, and protein malnutrition in particular, among the vulnerable groups of the rural peoples of China, as in any other part of rural Asia. This is reflected in high rates of infant and maternal mortality and

TABLE 19.   Levels of Adequacy of Calories and Proteins in Asian Diets

Nutrition grade	Calories	Animal protein	Legume and foodgrain protein
A	Adequate	Adequate	Present, but not essential as source of protein
B	Adequate	Becoming scarce	Become essential as source of protein
Below this level diet is unlikely to be adequate for vulnerable groups			
C	Adequate	Absent	Only sources of protein
D	Adequate	Absent	Grain legumes become inadequate, therefore balance in dietary protein deteriorates
E	Calories maintained at minimum requirement by State action or international aid	Absent	Grain legumes insignificant, dietary protein from foodgrains unbalanced.
F	Calories always or seasonally inadequate	Absent	Foodgrain protein used as calories

Source: Compiled by author.

deaths of children of pre-school age; low birth weights; low growth rates (weight, height, skeletal development) from six months, which may persist to maturity; high degree of susceptibility and low resistance to gastro-intestinal and respiratory diseases and other infections; impaired neuromotor development; limited life-span and premature senescence, particularly of women. The apathy, lethargy and lack of initiative for which the Asian worker is so often blamed are due in large part to malnutrition from early life. Clinical and biochemical investigations will reveal evidence of multiple deficiency of nutrients.

In considering the emphasis to be given in essential welfare programmes, it is realistic to recognize that a drastic reduction in the death rate of children will, in the absence of family planning, create even greater problems later—in the provision of food, housing and employment for a larger mature population.

It has been shown in Chapter I that the overall characteristics and crises of a monsoonal environment apply just as much to China as to the other countries in the region. Into this pan-Asian category come the epidemic and endemic diseases which must be tackled not by mere exhortation and incantation, but by the methods which have been adopted in Asian medical science. A scientific approach must also be adopted in the recognition and treatment of diseases which are the manifestation of, or are aggravated by nutritional deficiencies.

XIII
Social and Political Implications

Iт has already been shown that there is a close relation between protein nutrition from conception to five years of age, and the development of the brain. The most significant question in nutrition research throughout the world at the present time is whether, as seems increasingly apparent, early protein deprivation is responsible for impaired mental capacity subsequently to acquire and use knowledge and experience. If this is so, one must visualize vast populations of intellectually stunted and malleable human material, ideal for political regimentation and manipulation by a ruling élite. This situation differs from the past particularly in scale, although the causes are different.

On the basis of his work for USAID in India, Berg (1967) has stated:

New evidence suggesting a relationship between malnutrition and mental retardation should be cause for major policy concern in a number of world capitals. The recognition that malnourished children may emerge from childhood lacking the ability to reach their full genetic intellectual potential introduces a new and perhaps frightening note into theories of national development.

The implications are ominous. For many years we have assumed that, given educational opportunities and environmental advantages, each normally born infant has every prospect of growing up to be bright and productive. It is now suggested that malnourished children may be basically dull. The significance of this can be appreciated when we recognize that as many as two-thirds of the children of most developing countries are now suffering from some degree of malnutrition. The relation of malnutrition to mental growth dramatizes the issue .... Dr. C. Gopalan[1] reports that 80 per cent of pre-school aged children in the rural areas of his country suffer from malnutritional dwarfism. The effect of this on productivity and the limits it places on the individual's potential contribution to his society are obvious.

The FAO/WHO/UNICEF Protein Advisory Group quotes a statement of the U.N. Advisory Committee on Science and Technology, on the importance of adequate nutrition for the preschool child (United Nations, 1970).

During a brief period after birth the brain of warm-blooded creatures can build 'by imprint' a permanent capability to synthesize in the brain certain enzymes required for the manufacture of chemicals which are essential for future brain formation, for instance the capacity to cope with mental stress and to build up a behaviour pattern. This time is short—hours for birds, months for monkeys, and as long as a few years for humans. When this short period of time expires, the capacity to build such a capability 'by imprint' is lost forever.

Two influences are essential in order that this critically important process may occur; firstly, affection and attention from 'parents' and social group, and secondly, an adequate diet, particularly protein. Continuing progress in brain research is providing each year additional insights into these complex functions of the brain. We do not yet know certainly how long this 'imprint receptivity' lasts, but it is certainly not more than a few years after birth.

The Committee insisted on the necessity that adequate protein for pre-school children should receive the highest priority in all programmes aimed at meeting the protein crisis. It stated that the irreparable damage now being inflicted on protein-malnourished children all over the world must be a matter of grave concern to all humanity.

On the basis of a review of all existing knowledge up to the end of 1969, FAO (1969) concludes:

In children, severe malnutrition (protein-calorie malnutrition and marasmus) during the first two years of life may adversely and permanently affect head circumference and brain size. Malnutrition appears also to be associated with permanently impaired intellectual performance, but evidence that this association is one of cause and effect is still lacking. It is difficult in man to separate the effects due to nutritional factors from those due to other environmental factors, of social, economic and cultural nature. There is evidence that in children, as in animals, the effects of malnutrition are related to its timing, duration and severity .... Although it is as yet impossible in human beings to dissociate malnutrition from other environmental factors of socio-economic nature, it must be remembered that the association of malnutrition with poor socio-economic level will persist. Hence, we may now be facing the situation where ... early malnutrition and

---

[1] Director, Nutrition Research Laboratories, Indian Council of Medical Research, Hyderabad, Andhra Pradesh.

therefore mental retardation and possibly permanent damage in young children and infants are bound eventually
to have cumulative effects on economic development. The
need, therefore, is to plan to avert such a possible unfortunate situation without necessarily waiting for it to be
proven.

This 'unfortunate situation' is not, however,
something which is going to happen in the future.
Malnutrition of the vulnerable groups has been
characteristic of the densely populated areas of
Asia for centuries. Only now are we beginning to
understand its true implications.

Unless and until reliable evidence to the contrary becomes available from the Chinese People's
Republic, it must be assumed that these state-
ments and this profound concern should apply
with equal force to the rural peoples of China.

Many people have suggested that all available
foods should be shared equitably among the different socio-economic groups of society. It is,
however, generally agreed that available supplies
of protein and other essential nutrients in Monsoon Asia are not sufficient to ensure a minimal
effective diet on this basis. One must accept that
diets will continue to be on a selective rather than
a universal basis:

(a) universal: equitable division of all available
     food resources which, being in deficit, pro-
     vide an unbalanced diet for all;
(b) selective: superior quality of diet ensured to
     those with certain responsibilities requiring
     greater intellectual ability; maintenance diet
     for the majority of the population, especially
     in rural areas. This is in fact the actual situa-
     tion, for socio-economic reasons, everywhere.
     With the increasing degree of imbalance to
     be expected between human populations and
     their food resources in respect particularly
     of quality, the ruling class must increasingly
     become a hereditary, nutritionally privileged

elite, or lose the mental capacity for leader-
ship.

No realistic political ideology has yet achieved,
or even aimed at, equality of nutrition. A theore-
tical classless society, in nutritional terms, is possible only when quality foods are in ample and
cheap supply from domestic production and/or
import.

Applied to China, this means that correctly
balanced nutrition, particularly in early life, is essential for the realization of the full genetic potential of those who will become responsible for
the scientific, managerial and administrative di-
rection of the vast resources of energy and inge-
nuity of the rural people, on which so much re-
liance is now being placed.

The economic and intellectual future of many
developing countries now requires that top priority should be given to the vulnerable groups in
the allocation of scarce resources, particularly of
protein foods. Realizing the true situation with
regard to availability of protein, the Government
of India has, through its Children's Charter, pro-
posed concentrating these limited resources upon
the pre-school children. The National Coordinat-
ing Committee on Food and Nutrition of the
Philippines has prepared a national programme to
combat malnutrition, which aims at the correct
nutrition of pregnant and nursing mothers, young
children and adolescents.

It would seem inconceivable that those responsible for food policy in China are not fully aware
of the importance of adequate nutrition in early
life for the future development of the State. There
is, however, no evidence to show that the necessary priority is being given to the vulnerable
groups in the allocation of those essential foods
which are becoming progressively more deficient
as population increases.

Bibliography

ADAMS, A.R.D. and MAEGRAITH, B.G. (1964). *Clinical tropical diseases.* 4th ed. Blackwell, London. 582 pp.

ADOLPH, W.H. (1949). 'Some aspects of nutrition research in China.' *Sci. Technol. China* 2: 80-83.

AFONSKY, D. (1949). 'The oral manifestations in 75 cases of vitamin B complex deficiency.' *Chinese Med. J.* 67: 243-51.

AIRD, J.S. (1968). *Estimates and projections of the population of mainland China, 1953-86.* U.S. Bureau of Census Series P. 91-17. Washington. 73 pp.

ANG, Jiak Woon. (1960). *Tables of representative values of foods commonly used in Singapore.* Department of Social Medicine and Public Health, University of Singapore.

AYKROYD, W.R. and DOUGHTY, J. (1964). *Legumes in human nutrition.* F.A.O. Nutrition Studies No. 19. Rome. 138 pp.

BARDHAN, P.K. (1970). 'Chinese and Indian agriculture: a broad comparison of recent policy and performance.' *J. Asian Studies,* 29: 515-37.

BERG, A.D. (1967). 'Malnutrition and national development.' *Foreign Affairs,* October. 126-36.

BOTHA-ANTOUN, E., BABAYAN, S. and HARFOUCHE, J.K. (1968). 'Intellectual development relating to nutritional status.' *J. Trop. Pediat.* 14: 112-15.

BOWERS, J.Z. (1970). 'Medicine in mainland China: Red and rural.' *Current Scene,* Hong Kong, 8: 12: 1-11.

BROCK, J.F. and AUTRET, M. (1952). *Kwashiorkor in Africa.* W.H.O. Monograph Series No. 8. World Health Organization, Geneva. 78 pp.

BUCK, J. Lossing. (1937). *Land utilization in China.* Commercial Press, Shanghai. 494 pp. Reprinted by Paragon Book Reprint Co., New York, 1964.

CHAMPAKAM, S., SRIKANTIA, S.G. and GOPALAN, C. (1968). 'Kwashiorkor and mental development.' *Amer. J. Clin. Nutrition.* 21: 844-52.

CHANDRASEKHAR, S. (1967). 'Marx, Malthus and Mao.' *Current Scene,* Hong Kong, 5: 3: 1-14.

CHANG, JEN-HU. (1971). 'The Chinese monsoon.' *Geogr. Rev.* 61: 370-95.

CHEN, Nai-ruenn. (1966). *Chinese economic statistics—a handbook for mainland China.* Edinburgh University Press. 539 pp.

CH'EN, J.S. and LI, O.L. (n.d.) *Composition of Chinese foods.* Department of Biochemistry, National Defence Medical Center, Taipei. 38 pp.

CHINA MEDICAL SCIENCE ACADEMY, LABOUR HEALTH, ENVIRONMENT HEALTH AND NUTRITION HEALTH RESEARCH INSTITUTE. (1963). *Table showing the components of food.* People's Health Press, Peking.

CHURCHILL, J.A., NEFF, J.W. and CALDWELL, D.F. (1966). 'Birth weight and intelligence.' *Obstetrics and Gynaecology* 28: 425-29.

CRAVIOTO, J., BIRCH, H.G., DE LICARDIE, E., ROSALES, L. and VEGA, L. (1969). 'The ecology of growth and development in a Mexican preindustrial community. 1. Method and findings from birth to one month of age.' *Soc. Res. in Child Development* 34: 5: 1-76.

——DE LICARDIE, E.R. and BIRCH, H.G. (1966). 'Nutrition, growth and neurointegrative development: an experimental and ecologic study.' *Pediatrics* 36: 319-72.

——GAONA, C.E., and BIRCH, H.G. (1967). 'Early malnutrition and auditory-visual integration in school-age children.' *J. Special Education* 2: 75-82.

——PINERO, C., ARROYO, M. and ALCADE, E. (1969). 'Mental performance of school children who suffered malnutrition in early age.' *Swedish Nutrition Foundation Symposia* 7: 85-91.

DAO, Shih-yen and CHEN, Lung-shun: (1957). 'The structure of the general circulation over the Asiatic continent in summer.' *Acta Meteorol. Sinica* 28: 234-47.

DAVIDSON, S. and PASSMORE, R. (1966). *Human nutrition and dietetics* (3rd ed.) E. and S. Livingstone, Edinburgh and London. 864 pp.

DAWSON, O.L. (1966). In *Food and agriculture in Communist China* (eds. J.L. Buck, O.L. Dawson and Wu Yuan-li). F.A. Praeger, New York/Pall Mall Press, London. 171 pp.

DIAMOND, N. (1969). *K'un Shen, a Taiwan village.* Holt, Rinehart and Winston. New York. 110 pp.

DONNITHORNE, A. (1970). *China's grain: output, procurement, transfers and trade.* Chinese University of Hong Kong, Economic Research Center. 36 pp.

EBERHARD, W. (1969). *A history of China* (3rd ed.). University of California Press, Berkeley and Los Angeles. 367 pp.

FEI, Hsiao-Tung. (1939). *Peasant life in China.* Kegan Paul, Trench, Trubner and Co. London. 300 pp.

FIELD, R.M. (1968). 'How much grain does Communist China produce?' *China Quarterly* 33: 98-107.

—— (1969). 'A note on the population of Communist China.' *China Quarterly* 38: 158-63.

FLOWERS, W.S. (1948). 'Causes of blindness in China.' *Chinese Med. J.* 66: 38-46.

FOOD AND AGRICULTURE ORGANIZATION OF THE UNITED NATIONS. (1949). *Food composition tables for international use (calories, protein, fat, carbohydrate).* Nutritional Study no. 3. F.A.O., Rome.

—— (1954). *Food composition tables (minerals and vitamins).* Nutritional Study no. 11. F.A.O., Rome.

—— (1965). *Protein requirements: Report of a Joint F.A.O./W.H.O. Expert Group.* F.A.O. Nutrition Meetings Report Series No. 37. F.A.O., Rome. 71 pp.

—— (1966). 'Soybean acceptability and consumer adoptability in relation to food habits in different parts of the world.' Paper for International Conference on Soybean Foods, Peoria. Nutrition Division, F.A.O., Rome. mimeo. 8 pp.

—— (1967). 'Soybean: production, cultivation, economics of supply, processing and marketing.' *F.A.O./W.H.O./U.N.I.C.E.F. Protein Advisory Group Bulletin* no. 7: 25-44.

—— (1969a). *Food composition tables: annotated bibliography.* Nutrition Information Documents Series no. 1. FAO, Rome. 168 pp.

—— (1969b). 'Nutrition and mental development.' *Nutrition Newsletter* 7: 66-68.

—— (1970). *Amino acid content of foods and biological data on proteins.* F.A.O., Rome.

FREEDMAN, M. (1958). *Lineage organization in southeastern China.* Athlone Press, London. 154 pp.

—— (1966). *Chinese lineage and society: Fukien and Kwangtung.* Athlone Press, London. 207 pp.

FUKUTAKE, T. (1967). *Asian rural society: China, India, Japan.* University of Tokyo Press. 207 pp.

GUTHRIE, H., GUTHRIE, G. and TAYAG, A. (1969). 'Nutritional status and intellectual performance in a rural Philippine community.' *Philippine J. Nutrition* 22: 2-10.

HER MAJESTY'S STATIONERY OFFICE. (1962). *Tables of representative values of foods commonly used in tropical countries.* Medical Research Council (London) Special Report Series no. 302.

HO, PING-TI. (1959). *Studies on the population of China.* Harvard East Asian Studies. 341 pp.

HOU, CHI-MING. (1968). 'Sources of agricultural growth in Communist China.' *J. Asian Studies* 28: 721-37.

HSU, F.L.K. (1949). *Under the ancestors' shadow.* Routledge and Kegan Paul, London. 317 pp.

HUANG, PING-WEI. (1961). 'The complex natural zonation of China.' *U.S.S.R. Academy of Sciences Geographical Series* 1, 25-39. Quoted in Buchanan, K., (1970). *The transformation of the Chinese earth,* G. Bell and Sons, London. 336 pp.

HUECK, O. (1952). 'Beriberi in Tungkun, south China.' *Ztschr. Tropenmed. Parasitol.* 4: 127-30.

HUNT, R.C. (1968). 'Faith in the fields.' *Far Eastern Economic Review,* February 8, 225-27.

INDIAN COUNCIL OF MEDICAL RESEARCH. (1969). *Annual report, 1968-69,* New Delhi. 196 pp.

ISHIKAWA, S. (1967). *Economic development in Asian perspective.* Kinokuniya Bookstore, Tokyo.

JELLIFFE, D.B. (1968). *Infant nutrition in the subtropics and tropics.* (2nd ed.) World Health Organization, Geneva. 335 pp.

KARNOW, S. (1968). In *China readings: 3. Communist China* (ed. F. Schurmann and O. Schell). Pelican, Harmondsworth, England. 647 pp.

KE, C.L. (1947). 'Nutritional status of school

students in north China.' *Chinese J. Nutrition* 2: 13-20.

KLATT, W. (1970). 'A review of China's economy in 1970.' *China Quarterly* 43: 100-117.

LEBAR, F.M., HICKEY, G.C. and MUSGRAVE, J.K. (1964). *Ethnic groups of mainland southeast Asia.* H.R.A.F., Yale University, New Haven. 288 pp.

LEE, C.C. (1948). 'Birth weights of full-term infants in west China.' *Chinese Med. J.* 66: 153-55.

LIANG, C.S. (1964). 'A study on water resource development in the Three Gorges of the Yangtze River.' *Chung Chi Journal,* Hong Kong, 4: 1: 42-56.

——(1965). 'Three types of agricultural water use in the Yangtze Basin.' *Chung Chi Journal,* 5: 1: 40-59

LIN, YUEH-HWA. (1948). *The golden wing: a sociological study of Chinese familism.* Kegan Paul, Trench, Trubner and Co. London. 234 pp.

LIU, TA-CHUNG and YEH, KUNG-CHIA. (1965). *The economy of the Chinese mainland: national income and economic development, 1933-59.* Princeton University Press. 771 pp.

LOW, H. Brian, (1937). In *Land utilization in China,* (ed. J.L. Buck). pp. 437-72. Commercial Press, Shanghai.

MALENBAUM, W. (1959). 'India and China: contrasts in development performance.' *American Economic Review* 49: 284-309.

MALLORY, W.H. (1926). *China: Land of Famine.* American Geographical Society Special Publication no. 6. 199 pp.

MAYNARD, L.A, and SWEN, WENYUH (1937). 'Nutrition.' In *Land utilization in China* (ed. J.L. Buck). pp. 400-36. Commercial Press, Shanghai.

MYRDAL, G. (1968). *Asian drama: an inquiry into the poverty of nations.* N.Y. Twentieth Century Fund, New York. 3 vols. 2,284 pp.

MYRDAL, J. (1966). *Report from a Chinese village.* Heinemann, London and New American Library, New York. 397 pp.

NEEDHAM, J. and LU, G.-d. (1962). 'Hygiene and preventive medicine in ancient China.' *J. Hist. Med.* 17: 429-78.

ORLEANS, L.A. (1969). 'Propheteering: the population of Communist China.' *Current Scene,* Hong Kong 7: 24: 13-19.

PLATT, B.S. (1968). In *Infant nutrition in the subtropics and tropics* (D.B. Jelliffe). W.H.O., Geneva. 335 pp.

RAJ, K.N. (1967). *India, Pakistan and China: economic growth and outlook.* Allied Publishers, New Delhi. 100 pp.

RAJALAKSHMI, R. (1969). 'Biochemistry of mental disorders with special reference to dietary factors.' Working paper to W.H.O. Expert Committee on Biochemistry of Mental Disorders. University of Baroda, mimeo. 19 pp.

RICHARDSON, S.D. (1966). *Forestry in Communist China.* Johns Hopkins Press, Baltimore. 179 pp.

SANDOSHAM, A.A. (1969). 'Malaria in rural Malaya.' *Med. J. Malaya* 24: 221-26.

SNYDER, C. (1970). 'Malthus versus Marx.' *Far Eastern Economic Review* 69: 52: 28-32.

SUNDARARAJ, R., BEGUM, A., JESUDIAN, G. and PEREIRA, S.M. (1969). 'Seasonal variation in the diets of pre-school children in a village (North Arcot District). I. Calories, protein, fat.' *Indian J. Med. Res.* 57: 249-59. 'II. Vitamins, minerals.' *Indian J. Med. Res.* 57: 375-83.

SWAMY, S. and BURKI, S.J. (1970). 'Foodgrains output in P.R.C., 1958-65.' *China Quarterly* 40: 58-63.

TENG, C.C. (1963). 'The demarcation of the agricultural regions of China.' *Acta Geographica Sinica,* December. Quoted in Buchanan, K. (1970). *The transformation of the Chinese earth.* G. Bell and Sons, London. 336 pp.

THOMSON, F.A., RUIZ, E. and BAKAR, M (1964). 'Vitamin A and protein deficiency in Malayan children.' *Trans. R. Soc. trop. Med. Hyg.* 58: 425-31.

TOPLEY, M. (1970). 'Chinese traditional ideas and treatment of disease: two examples from Hong Kong.' *Man* 5: 421-37.

TREGEAR, T.R. (1965). *A geography of China.* London University Press. 342 pp.

UNITED NATIONS. Advisory Committee on Science and Technology. (1970). 'Statement on importance of adequate nutrition for the pre-school child.' *Protein Advisory Group Bulletin* no. 9: 22-23.

UNITED STATES DEPARTMENT OF AGRICULTURE.

(1952). *Composition of foods used in Far Eastern countries.* Agriculture Handbook no. 34.

WANG, CHI-WU. (1961). *The forests of China.* Maria Moors Cabot Foundation Publication Series No. 5. Harvard, Mass. 313 pp.

WANG, Y.C. (1947). 'Dietary survey in Lichung.' *Chinese J. Nutrition* 2: 21-32.

WASHENKO, S. (1969). 'Agriculture in mainland China—1968.' *Current Scene,* Hong Kong 7: 6: 1-2.

WENMOHS, J.R. (1967). 'Agriculture in mainland China—1967.' *Current Scene,* Hong Kong, 6: 21: 1-12.

WHYTE, R.O. (1967). *Milk production in developing countries.* Faber and Faber, London/F.A. Praeger, New York. 240 pp.

——(1968a). *Land, livestock and human nutrition in India.* F.A. Praeger, New York and London. 309 pp.

——(1968b). *Grasslands of the monsoon.* Faber and Faber, London/F.A. Praeger, New York, 325 pp.

——(1970). 'Livestock planning for Monsoon Asia.' *SPAN* (Shell International) 13: 37-41.

——(1972). *Rural nutrition in Monsoon Asia.* Oxford University Press, Kuala Lumpur.

——and MATHUR, M.L. (1968). *The planning of milk production in India.* Orient Longmans, New Delhi. 221 pp.

WINICK, M. (1969). 'Malnutrition and brain development.' *J. Pediatrics* 74: 667-69.

——and ROSSO, P. (1969). 'Head circumference and cellular growth of the brain in normal and marasmic children.' *J. Pediatrics* 74: 774-78.

WOLF, M. (1968). *The house of Lim.* Appleton-Century-Crofts, New York. 147 pp.

WOLFF, R.J. (1962). *Food habits in Malaya.* University of California, mimeo. 25 pp.

WORLD HEALTH ORGANIZATION. (1969). *The health aspects of food and nutrition.* W.H.O. Western Pacific Regional Office, Manila. 380 pp.

WU, HUNG-SHUN and CHEN, LUNG-SHUN. (1956). 'The structure of general circulation over Asia from January to the first decade of March, 1956.' *Acta Meteorol. Sinica* 27: 361-81.

YANG, C.K. (1959). *A Chinese village in early Communist transition.* M.I.T. (Massachusetts Institute of Technology) Press. 284 pp.

YANG, M.C. (1945). *A Chinese village: Taitou, Shantung Province.* Columbia University Press, New York. 275 pp.

YEH, KUNG-SHAO. (1959). 'Physical growth of Chinese children: a summary of work done during the past half century.' *Chinese Med. J.* 78: 439-45.

Index